G000061491

CONTENTS

Dear Reader

Welcome to the World Chocolate Awards guide book.

Six hundred and sixty milk and white chocolates from all over the world have been evaluated over the last three and a half years, in order to select the best. Awards are given solely for taste, and only chocolates which have received an award are listed in this guide. Every chocolate is evaluated using consistent and objective standards which are designed to avoid any kind of bias. It is left to the reader to decide upon personal preferences for flavour, or to select a chocolate to suit the taste of the person to whom they intend to give it. A list of all the chocolates that have been evaluated is available on the World Chocolate Awards website.

The World Chocolate Awards is the only impartial and independent mark of distinction for fine chocolate in the world. Its purpose is to serve the interests of the consumer. It does not accept funding, free bars of chocolate or incentives from the chocolate industry. There never has been a business, friend or family connection between those involved in the World Chocolate Awards and chocolate brands, their public relations agents, or promoters.

The World Chocolate Awards process involves five stages:

RESEARCH — Worldwide research is carried out to identify as many chocolates as possible that meet two qualifying criteria. First, the chocolate must be unique: it must have been made from the cacao beans by the brand selling it, or be exclusive to the brand selling it. Second, the chocolate must not contain substitute ingredients to reduce the cost of its manufacture, such as vegetable fat, vanilla flavour or vanilla extract.

ACQUISITION — The methods the World Chocolate Awards use to purchase products ensure that it evaluates the same chocolate that is available to the public and that there is no possibility of receiving specially produced or selected items.

EVALUATION — To avoid bias and ensure effective evaluation, standards are applied to ensure the optimal storage of chocolate, a clean palate for tasting, an ideal environment for tasting, an ample time frame, a suitable quantity of each chocolate and consistent, objective records. Every chocolate is evaluated on several occasions by a full time professional to determine its taste characteristics and grade it (from one to a maximum of ten points) for its taste. Chocolates which are graded with eight, nine, or ten points are awarded one, two or three stars respectively and listed in the World Chocolate Awards guide book.

INFORMATION GATHERING — Brands whose chocolate has been awarded stars are contacted in order to gather information for the World Chocolate Awards guide book. Where it is practical to do so, a meeting is arranged in order to take exclusive photos and gather information first hand. Relevant photos, books or brochures may be accepted by the World Chocolate Awards. Entry in the World Chocolate Awards is completely free of charge and free of any obligation to participate in the information gathering process. Brands can not choose to be excluded from the World Chocolate Awards.

PUBLICATION The World Chocolate Awards guide book is published every four years. A complimentary copy is given to each brand that is listed in the World Chocolate Awards guide where it is practical to do so.

HOW TO USE THE GUIDE

Chocolates are listed in order of the country that they are made in, then by brand.

Stars are awarded for taste. They are displayed next to the brand name, beneath the name of the chocolate.

✹✹✹ One of the greatest chocolates of the world, prized for its taste.
✹✹ One of the best chocolates of the world, prized for its taste.
✹ An outstanding chocolate with excellent taste.

[The brand] say The description of a chocolate begins with a quote from the World Chocolate Awards intended to inspire the curiosity of the reader to whom the particular chocolate may appeal. Next is a quote from the brand regarding their chocolate. In some cases it has been translated.

Cacao The type of cacao used to make the chocolate and the location where it was grown, if this information has been disclosed.

Established The date that the brand was first established and other historical facts.

Made The location where the chocolate is moulded. If the term "cacaofèvier" is written next to the brand name (on the right edge of the right page) the chocolate is also made from the dried cacao beans at this location.

Interestingly Curious facts relevant to chocolate or the brand and its products.

Milk chocolate/White chocolate A factual description of the chocolate and its key ingredients. Unless stated otherwise the chocolate is made with cow's milk. The chocolate is free from vanilla unless it is stated. Chocolates with no added sugar are also identified here.

The strength of key tastes perceived is indicated by dots. This is not a list of ingredients.
●●● Intense
●● Medium
● Mild

% The factual content of cocoa or other key ingredients is stated as a percentage.

Taste A list of flavours that might be perceived when tasting the chocolate. This is not a list of ingredients. Everyone interprets tastes differently, so the list has two uses: first, the types of flavours listed provide insight into the general character of the chocolate; second, the reader may enjoy comparing the flavours on the list with those that they perceive when tasting the chocolate.

At the back of the book is an "Ingredient Index" which allows the reader to search for chocolates made from certain key ingredients.

CHOCOLATE
TERMS

AFTERTASTE   A taste remaining after food has been swallowed. If the taste persists in the mouth for a long time it may be described as a "long aftertaste" or "long finish."

ADDED INGREDIENT   Any ingredient added to **chocolate**. For example vanilla, hazelnut, salt. Sugar and **cocoa butter** are optional ingredients of chocolate and are not added ingredients.

ARRIBA   Unique taste that **cacao** harvested from **forastero** "nacional" trees grown in Ecuador may, or may not, have. Cacao with the arriba taste is one of the most prized in the world because of its floral qualities and low bitterness. Nobody has successfully reproduced the arriba taste by cultivating forastero nacional in other lands. The reason may be the particular soil and climate of Ecuador. Not all cacao or chocolate sold under the name "arriba" necessarily has the unique taste that is being claimed. "Arriba" (Spanish for "up") was coined in the early 19th century when locals referred to cacao of a special taste that was brought to the buyers in the city of Guayaquil, Ecuador, as from "up" the Guayas river. Arriba was never used to refer to all forastero nacional, or all cacao grown in Ecuador.

BEAN TO BAR   The whole process of making a chocolate bar starting with dried **cacao** beans. These words appear in the marketing material of many brands that are not **bean to bar chocolate makers**. Although every chocolate bar must go through this process, not every chocolate maker or **chocolatier** carries out the whole process of making chocolate from the bean to the bar themselves.

BEAN TO BAR CHOCOLATE MAKER   Person or brand who themselves carries out the whole process of making bars of **chocolate** starting with dried **cacao** beans. Some bean to bar chocolate makers use **cocoa butter** which they have separated themselves. Others purchase the cocoa butter. Only a small proportion of **chocolatiers** are bean to bar chocolate makers.

BLEND   Chocolate made from more than one **origin** of **cacao** bean.

BLENDING   Mixing more than one **origin** of **cacao** together during any stage of the chocolate making process by mixing beans, **nibs**, **liqueurs**, **cocoa powders** or melted chocolates. Some **chocolatiers** melt and mix together different chocolates that they have purchased to create their own blend of chocolate. This allows them to have some influence over the taste of the chocolate that they sell despite not being involved in the earlier stages of chocolate manufacture. There are three possible reasons for blending: 1. To create a taste that is not achievable using any single origin of cacao. An example being Amedei's "9" chocolate which is a blend of nine different cacao origins. 2. To create a consistent taste for the consumer. 3. To improve the taste of one or more of the elements blended. For example to compromise between cost and taste, or to make use of cocoa that otherwise would not be palatable. Blended chocolate is not intrinsically superior or inferior to chocolate made from cacao from a single origin: every chocolate must be evaluated on its own merit.

BLOOM
An unappealing whitish coating on the surface of chocolate caused by the formation of **cocoa butter** crystals that have escaped from the chocolate because it was temporarily exposed to heat, or by the formation of sugar crystals because it was temporarily exposed to moisture. Bloom is produced when chocolate is not kept consistently in the correct temperature or humidity range, for example when chocolate is taken from an air-conditioned shop into a warm car, or from a fridge into a warm room. Another cause of cocoa butter bloom is imperfect **tempering**. Cocoa butter bloom can be resolved by tempering bloomed chocolate again. Bloom only affects the surface of chocolate. It is not aesthetically pleasing and the original surface texture is lost, but it is edible. If a chocolate has other abnormalities, something in addition to bloom has occurred. To avoid bloom and other problems chocolate should be kept in its wrapper in an airtight odourless container in a dark, cool, dry place. Generally, glass containers are odourless and plastic containers are not. Different chocolates should be kept in different containers. The temperature should be consistent between 14-18°C. Chocolate should be brought slowly to room temperature for tasting whilst it is still inside its airtight container. If this is not possible try insulating it by other means, for example wrapping it in a thick towel.

CACAO
The cacao tree (with the botanical name Theobroma cacao) its fruit (pods) or its seeds (beans). Cacao beans are the fundamental raw material used to make chocolate. The tropical American evergreen tree may grow over 15m high and live for over fifty years. It bears pods all year, although at some times it is more productive than others. The colour, size and shape of the pod vary according to the genetic variety (**genotype**). Ripe pods can measure 12-30cm long and can be identified because they have changed colour. Inside the pod are thirty to seventy cacao beans coated in a whitish or yellowish pulp. The beans are as big as, or twice the size of, an almond. They may also be almond shaped, flat, cylindrical or oval. Since the Spanish conquest of America the cacao tree has become cultivated around the world within the range of about twenty degrees north and south of the equator, an area for which the term "the cacao belt" has been coined.

The name "cacao" is a Spanish corruption of an ancient Central American name (possibly "kakawa") for the tree and its produce. Within the Theobroma cacao species there are many known genetic varieties (genotypes) all of which can be used to make chocolate. The genotype of a cacao tree is identified by analysis of its DNA, a costly procedure that has recently become more widespread. New genotypes are being hunted and identified every year in the old plantations and tropical forests of Central America and northern South America. It is certain that there are many genotypes yet to be discovered. New **hybrid** genotypes also occur as the result of deliberate cross-breeding for improved yields and resistance to disease.

Because man discovered cacao over three thousand years before DNA, a confusing, inconsistent and inaccurate system of identifying cacao by **phenotype** (visually observable characteristics such as the pod or bean shape or colour) has long been in use. To the dismay of scientists, the widespread use of phenotype has not been replaced with genotype. The three names commonly used to describe cacao phenotypes are Spanish:

forastero, criollo and trinitario. **Forastero** (meaning foreign) and **criollo** (pronounced "cree-yo-yo" meaning native) are relative to the person using them and where he is. One man's native cacao tree is a visiting man's foreign tree. **Trinitario** (meaning from Trinidad) is more specific but it refers to any cacao from the island. Many different cacao genotypes are present on the island. To confuse matters more, the name trinitario is commonly used to refer to cacao that has no connection with the island. Cacao geneticist Basil Bartley observed in 2005 that the name trinitario is "used as a sort of mental waste bin for unclassifiable material." The link between the name trinitario and Trinidad is as follows: the name trinitario was inconsistently used to refer to cacao that was introduced from Trinidad to countries in the New World and Old World many times during the last four hundred years. Some of this cacao was forastero, some was criollo and others were the product of hybridisation on the island between forastero and criollo. In recent history the name trinitario has most commonly been used to refer to the hybrids. In the absence of any other common classification than forastero and criollo, any cacao with hybrid characteristics has also been called trinitario.

The most consistent and useful meanings inferred by the use of the three phenotype names are:

Forastero: cacao tree bearing beans that are of a dark colour when raw.

Criollo: cacao tree bearing beans that are of a whitish or very light colour when raw.

Trinitario: cacao tree bearing beans that are a mix of the above two characteristics. This occurs because it is a hybrid between criollo and forastero.

Forastero is the most cultivated cacao in the world, accounting for about 80% of production. There are five reasons why this is so: 1. It happened to arrive to the right place at the right time. Forastero was the main cacao introduced from America to West Africa and South East Asia in the 1800's. In 2012 Africa produced 73% of the world's cacao. 2. Forastero can provide a high yield. 3. Forastero can be more resistant to some diseases and conditions. 4. Forastero is used by almost all **cacaofèviers** in the world. 5. There is insufficient financial motivation to cultivate other phenotypes.

The average person has only tasted chocolate made with forastero cacao, or forastero **blended** with a small quantity of other cacao phenotypes. Criticism of the taste of forastero and praise for that of trinitario and criollo is found in almost every description of the three phenotypes. But forastero cacao does not have an intrinsic taste: it is a name given to any cacao that has specific visible characteristics. Neither does forastero have less flavour than other cacao. Chocolate made from each cacao phenotype simply tastes different. And within each particular type an extraordinary range of different tastes can be found due to variations in genetics, soil, weather and all the stages of processing the beans into chocolate. Ultimately every chocolate must be evaluated on its own merit.

Criollo makes up less than 10% of the world's cacao production. Trinitario makes up less than 20% of the world's cacao production.

CACAOFÈVIER   Person or brand that makes **chocolate** from dried cacao beans. The word cacaofèvier, created by Michel Cluizel in 2006, translates literally as "cacao bean processor." It allows those who make chocolate starting with cacao beans to be distinguished from **chocolatiers**, because both may describe themselves as a "chocolate maker." Some cacaofèviers use **cocoa butter** which they have separated themselves. Others purchase cocoa butter.

CHOCOLATE   **Cocoa liqueur** (roasted and ground cocoa beans) or a product in which cocoa liqueur is the fundamental ingredient. Additional processing, **milling** or **conching** for example, is optional. Sugar and additional **cocoa butter** are optional.

In the European Union "chocolate" (which may be supplemented with the word "dark" or "plain") must contain, measured by weight, not less than: 35% total **cocoa content** including 18% cocoa butter and 14% of **cocoa solids**.

In the United States of America "chocolate," "plain chocolate" and "dark chocolate" are not defined. "Sweet chocolate" must contain, measured by weight: not less than 15% cocoa liqueur and less than 12% milk solids. "Semisweet chocolate" or "bittersweet chocolate" is defined as "sweet chocolate" that contains not less than 35% chocolate liqueur.

In Canada "chocolate" (which may be supplemented with the word "dark," "bittersweet," or "semi-sweet") must contain, measured by weight: not less than 35% cocoa content, of which not less than 18% is cocoa butter and not less than 14% is cocoa solids. It may contain less than 5% milk solids. "Sweet chocolate" must contain, measured by weight not less than 30% cocoa content, of which 18% is cocoa butter, and 12% is cocoa solids. It may contain less than 12% milk solids.

CHOCOLATIER   Also called a **chocolate maker**. Person or brand that completes the final stages in the production of chocolate (**tempering** and moulding chocolate) or the final stages in the production of filled chocolates (pralines, bonbons or truffles). Most chocolatiers buy chocolate in the form of buttons or large blocks that they melt to use. A very small number of chocolatiers are **cacaofèviers**.

COCOA   Cacao that has been **roasted**. Cocoa is the fundamental material used to make chocolate. It is composed of **cocoa solids** and **cocoa butter** in nearly equal proportions.

COCOA BUTTER   Whitish or yellowish edible fat obtained from roasted or unroasted cacao beans. It contains no dairy produce. Cocoa butter is an optional ingredient of **chocolate**. It is commonly added to **cocoa liqueur**, which naturally contains about 50% cocoa butter, during the production of chocolate for eating.

The additional cocoa butter modifies the taste and texture of chocolate. It helps to produce a smoother chocolate and can reduce the intensity of the

cocoa solids.

Cocoa butter is solid at room temperature and melts at body temperature. When tempered, cocoa butter makes it possible for solid chocolate to have a crisp texture. It also makes it possible for chocolate to melt in the mouth and contributes to the smooth and buttery sensations.

Cocoa butter is usually **deodorised** before it is used for any purpose. This is the name given to the process of reducing or removing the odour and taste of cocoa butter by exposing it to dry steam inside a vacuum. Deodorisation has several uses: cocoa butter separated from unpalatable beans may be made bland and palatable; cocoa butter with reduced odour and taste may be sold to the pharmaceutical and cosmetic industry; cocoa butter with a more consistent taste may be produced regardless of the natural taste of the cocoa butter which varies according to the beans from which it was separated; cocoa butter with a consistent taste facilitates efficient manufacture, consistent results and helps to create a product with a consistent taste for the consumer. Because most butter is deodorised, it is regarded as the norm. This is why the term **non-deodorised** is used to refer to cocoa butter which has not been deodorised and retains its natural taste. For an explanation of the common process for obtaining cocoa butter, see **cocoa solids**. Cocoa butter can be the most expensive ingredient in chocolate. In some chocolates it is partially substituted with other vegetable fats to reduce costs. Vegetable fat can not reproduce the sensation of cocoa butter in the mouth. The World Chocolate Awards does not regard chocolate made with substitute ingredients as fine chocolate and does not evaluate it.

COCOA CONTENT Total quantity of **cocoa solids** and **cocoa butter** in **chocolate**. It is measured as a percentage of the total weight of the chocolate. Cocoa content does not inform us of the ratio of cocoa solids to cocoa butter: two bars of chocolate with the same percentage cocoa content may have different quantities of each. However the ingredient list of a chocolate can indicate which one the ratio leans in favour of, because the list is in the order of largest quantity first. **Added ingredients** are not included in the cocoa content calculation because they are not an ingredient of "chocolate." For example the cocoa content of a chocolate will be the same whether hazelnuts have been added to it or not. The quality, colour, taste and bitterness of chocolate do not depend on its cocoa content. For example, the bitterness of chocolate is determined by numerous factors including: the condition and **origin** of the cacao used; the optional ingredients used; and the treatment of the ingredients during the many stages of the chocolate making process. From fermentation to tempering, almost every stage involves prolonged exposure to heat (cooking) and therefore the possibility of burning. Cocoa is particularly vulnerable during roasting. The deeper the roast the closer the beans get to being burnt and the more bitter their taste will be.

COCOA LIQUEUR Also called **liquor, cocoa mass, chocolate liqueur** and **chocolate**. The edible gritty brownish paste produced by grinding cocoa **nibs** in a **mill**. It contains no alcohol or **added ingredients**. Cocoa beans, cocoa nibs and cocoa liqueur are composed of **cocoa solids** and **cocoa butter** in nearly equal proportions. Because sufficient heat is generated by the friction of the grinding of the nibs to melt the cocoa butter in them, a paste and not a powder is produced. Cocoa liqueur (roasted and ground cacao beans) is chocolate. Additional processing is optional. Sugar and additional **cocoa butter** are optional.

COCOA SOLIDS   Also called **cocoa powder** or **defatted cocoa powder**. The brownish powder, too dry to eat, produced by grinding cocoa press cake. Press cake is the material remaining after **cocoa butter** has been pressed in a machine, under pressures as high as six thousand pounds per square inch, from **cocoa liqueur**. Because of the limitations of pressing cocoa, cocoa powder retains a cocoa butter content of 10-24%, but this is not enough to make it palatable and melt in the mouth. Cocoa powder is commonly used to make drinking chocolate (sugar and hot water or hot milk are normally added). Its reduced butter content avoids cocoa butter floating unsightly on top of the drink, which happens when cocoa liquor is used (an example of this may be seen in traditional Central American chocolate drinks, as illustrated on page 83). Cocoa powder is also used in baking and to coat filled chocolates (bonbons, truffles and pralines). An estimated one third of cocoa powder produced is reunited with cocoa butter to manufacture chocolate.

CONCHE   Machine used to expose **cocoa liqueur** to a small grinding action and to air by continually moving it to and fro in a heated trough with a stone or metal roller. It is named after the conche shell because of the shape of the original machine which was developed by Rodolphe Lindt in Switzerland in 1879. Nowadays the term "conche" is also used if this stage of the chocolate making process is carried out by a **mill**. Conching chocolate changes it: it does not necessarily make it better or worse. Conching is used to change the taste of chocolate and make its texture smoother by three actions. First, it reduces the size of particles. Second, it intimately mixes the particles of **cocoa solids**, **cocoa butter** and any optional ingredients in it, such as sugar. Third, it cooks the liqueur and enables some evaporation. Changes to taste can include the reduction of sourness and bitterness, if present. This promotes other tastes or other tastes develop. Over time, conching will ultimately reduce all tastes present in chocolate, making it blander. There is no universal correct length of time to conche for: the correct time is whatever is required to obtain the desired result. Andrea Slitti illustrated this when he said to us, "If you drive to Rome in a BMW and I cycle there, we will both arrive at Rome!" The length of time required is dependent on many variables: the taste and texture preferences of the operator; the conche machine; the temperature of everything; how fine the cocoa liquor has been ground; the cacao beans. After conching, chocolate can be **tempered** and moulded into bars. A conche is shown at the bottom of pages 255, 274 and 275.

LECITHIN   Usually a product of soybean that is used as an optional ingredient in chocolate to help the materials that chocolate is made of to mix together (emulsify) because they naturally separate. It can help to make chocolate more fluid. Lecithin is commonly added to chocolate in a quantity of less than 0.5% during the **conching** stage. Lecithin has been used for nearly a century as a substitute for adding extra cocoa butter (which also is an emulsifier) to chocolate to reduce costs, or to make a less buttery chocolate.

MILL   Machine used to reduce the particle size of **nibs** or **cocoa liqueur** by grinding. Nibs are ground until they become liqueur. Liqueur is ground until it becomes as fine as is required. Liqueur may be **conched**. Some mills are capable of grinding material through all of these stages. In other cases different specialised mills are used to grind finer material in each stage.

One type of mill is a **melangeur** (pronounced melon-jur, French for mixer) a horizontal circular tank with a revolving bedplate which has two stone or metal rolls resting on it. The rolls are driven round when the bedplate rotates. It is shown on pages 130, 131, 344 and 361.

A **roll mill** has stone or metal rolls between which material is ground. It is shown on pages 63 (top left), 137, 149 and 273 (lower left).

The process of grinding cocoa nibs between stones is essentially the same as that used by the ancient Central Americans. Their grinding stone, called a metate (pronounced meh-tah-tey) can still be found in use today. It is shown on pages 82, 83, 85 and 238.

A **ball mill** consists of a metal cylinder containing loose metal balls. The balls are stirred by a rotating shaft in the centre to grind cocoa nibs or beans amongst them into cocoa liqueur, or to grind and move cocoa liqueur to conche it. It is shown on page 266.

MILK CHOCOLATE   Product of which **cocoa liqueur** (roasted and ground cocoa beans) and milk solids (milk that has had most of the water separated from it) are the fundamental ingredients. Sugar and additional **cocoa butter** are optional.

In the European Union "milk chocolate" must contain, measured by weight, not less than: 25% **cocoa content**; 14% milk solids; 25% total fat (cocoa butter and milk fat, which is the natural fat of milk and chief constituent of butter). A maximum of 5% vegetable fat in addition to cocoa butter is permitted and will be declared in the ingredients list if used.

Additional rules apply to the United Kingdom and Ireland permitting "milk chocolate" to also be made to another specification with less cocoa and more milk. It must contain, measured by weight, no less than: 20% cocoa content; 20% milk solids; 2.5% cocoa solids; 5% milk fat; 25% total fat (cocoa butter and milk fat). In the rest of the European Union this is called "family milk chocolate." A maximum of 5% vegetable fat in addition to cocoa butter is permitted and will be declared in the ingredients list if used.

In the United States of America "milk chocolate" must contain, measured by weight, not less than: 10% chocolate liqueur; 39% milk fat (also known as butterfat, the natural fat of milk and chief constituent of butter); 12% milk solids.

In Canada "milk chocolate" must contain, measured by weight, not less than: 25% cocoa content, of which not less than 2.5% is fat-free cocoa solids; 15% cocoa butter; 12% milk solids; 3.39% milk fat.

NIBS   Nuts or cocoa beans that have been broken into pieces and separated from the shell. During the chocolate making process, cocoa nibs are ground until they become a paste called **cocoa liqueur**. In the United States of America cocoa nibs must not contain more than 1.75% shell by weight.

NO ADDED SUGAR   No added sugar (for example cane sugar, beet sugar or palm sugar) has been used to make the chocolate. Ingredients used to make the chocolate may contain naturally occurring sugars, for example milk and cocoa.

ORIGIN   Also called **terroir** (pronounced tair-rwah) in French. The location where the **cacao** was grown. "Single origin" means that all cacao beans used to make a chocolate are from one country, region, area, or plantation. Precise origin information, such as a plantation, has most value because the taste of cacao is partly determined by its genotype and the environment (climate and soil) that it grows in. It helps the consumer to understand, compare, record and express preferences. Knowing only the county of origin is not particularly useful because there are many plantations within most nations. "Single origin" chocolate is not intrinsically superior or inferior to chocolate with an undisclosed origin or multiple origins (**blends**). "Single origin" does not mean a single cacao genotype or phenotype was used: plantations often cultivate more than one type of cacao tree together.

ROASTING   Also called toasting. Cooking cacao by exposure to hot air or a hot surface. Roasting is a key process in the manufacture of chocolate. It is necessary to develop flavours. A variety of purpose built and adapted roasting machines are presently used in chocolate manufacture. They include ovens, rotating metal balls which hot air passes on the outside of, and rotating metal cylinders. The process is essentially the same as that used by the ancient Central Americans who roasted cacao on a clay plate over a fire.

The time and temperature that cacao beans are roasted for depends on numerous factors including the roasting machine, the type and size of the beans, their moisture content and the taste preferences of the cacaofèvier. Roasting often takes place after the cacao beans have been fermented, dried, transported to the factory and cleaned of debris. After roasting the beans are cooled down to prevent them continuing to cook, then broken and **winnowed**. The resulting **nibs** can be ground into **cocoa liqueur**. Alternatively roasting can take place after winnowing. By exposing the cacao beans to brief and intense heat they are not roasted but the shell dries and literally pops off. The beans are then broken into nibs, or ground into liqueur, either of which can be roasted. Although cacao is roasted in a dedicated machine, it must be noted that almost every stage of chocolate manufacture involves prolonged exposure to heat (cooking). If a raw beef steak was subjected to the same temperatures for the same period of time, skipping the roasting machine stage, it would be considered cooked. There is additional information on roasting under **cocoa content**.

TEMPERING   Process of heating and cooling chocolate, when it is in its melted liquid state, to crystallise the cocoa butter within it. This process, followed by proper cooling of the chocolate into a solid state, helps to prevent fat **bloom** and to produce chocolate with a crisp texture and glossy surface. Additional information on tempering can be found on page 132.

VANILLA   The orchid, its fruit, and the seeds contained within its fruit. The latter two are normally cured and used as an **added ingredient** to contribute a taste to chocolate. In some chocolates a vanilla substitute is used to reduce costs. Vanilla substitutes can not reproduce the taste of real vanilla. The World Chocolate Awards does not regard chocolate made with vanilla substitutes as fine chocolate and does not evaluate it. The following are vanilla substitutes: vanillin; vanilla extract; vanilla (natural flavour); vanilla (flavour); natural vanilla flavour; natural vanilla extract.

WHITE CHOCOLATE   Product in which **cocoa butter** and milk solids (milk that has had most of the water separated from it) are the fundamental ingredients. The addition of sugar is optional. **Vanilla** is a common **added ingredient** in white chocolate. White chocolate contains no, or almost no, **cocoa solids** (which are brown).

WINNOWING   To separate the thin brittle shells from roasted **cacao** beans, or flash heated **cacao** beans by the movement of air. This is done in three steps: the beans are broken into pieces; they are propelled into the air by vibration; air is blown across them to carry away shell fragments. The shells are lighter than the other material, which consists of broken pieces of bean husks (**nibs**). The shell of the cacao bean is normally not used in the production of chocolate because it does not benefit its taste or texture. A winnowing machine is shown on pages 39 and 369. Winnowing by hand is shown on page 82.

AUSTRALIA

PREMIUM MILK CHOCOLATE

Haigh's Chocolates ✿✿ ✿

A unique, instantly recognisable dense chocolate with delicious long, nutty, cocoa notes. **Haigh's say** We're very proud to be one of only a few specialist chocolate retailers in the world whose chocolate making still begins with the raw cacao bean. We insist on complete control from start to finish. **Cacao** Haigh's make their chocolate by blending two or three different types of cacao beans from different parts of the world. **Established** In 1915 by Alfred Haigh. The family still sells its chocolate from the original shop (pictured) in the historic Beehive Corner building in the centre of Adelaide's shopping district. There are now twelve Haigh's stores throughout Australia and over three hundred employees. The company is presently run by grandson John (right) and great-grandsons Alister and Simon (centre and left). **Made** In Adelaide.

Milk chocolate Blended with vanilla.

●●Cocoa 32%   ●●Sweet   ●●Milk   ●●Butter   ●Vanilla

Taste Hazelnut; chocolate cake; cashew; toffee; raisin; cream; nougat. Hint of cinnamon and spice.

MILK PEPPERMINT CHOCOLATE

Haigh's Chocolates ✵

Aromatic peppermint oil adds a bold and stimulating twist to Haigh's tangy and flavoursome chocolate. Although the balance leans in favour of the powerful peppermint, the cocoa is not far behind and retains considerable strength and detail. **Haigh's say** Roasting our own cacao beans allows us to develop our own unique blends of premium chocolate with distinct aroma, texture and flavour. **Cacao** A blend of two or three origins. **Interestingly** John Haigh brought European chocolate making machinery and expertise to Australia after studying at Lindt in Switzerland, in the 1950s. **Pictured** Haigh's moulded a chocolate Murray Cod (Australia's largest freshwater fish) to help raise funds towards the conservation of the country's longest river, the river Murray, which the fish inhabits. Left: chocolate truffles pass through a curtain of liquid chocolate on a conveyor grille, in order to enrobe them in chocolate. Next, they are decorated by hand (lower left) and conveyed though a tunnel of cool air to set them.

Milk chocolate Blended with vanilla and peppermint oil.

●●●Peppermint ●●Sweet ●●Cocoa 32% ●Milk ●Butter ●Vanilla

Taste Peppermint oil; hazelnut; chocolate cake; toffee; cream; nougat.

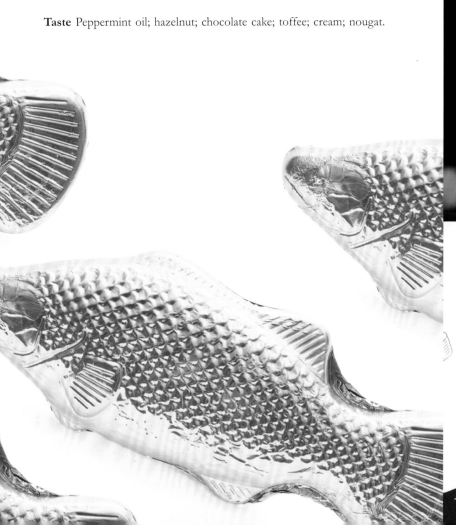

HAIGH'S CHOCOLATES DARK CHOCOLATE

ESTABLISHED 1915

HAIGH'S CHOCOLATE

PEPPERMINT

25

AUSTRIA

BOURBON VANILLE

Choco-Lina ✿

There are numerous rounded flavours to enjoy here, thanks to the use of light, lean and fragrant sheep milk, tangy raw cane sugar and non-deodorised cocoa butter. **Choco-Lina say** The first lactose-free white chocolate in the world. Quality ingredients like raw cane sugar, the finest cocoa beans, the purest sheep milk and very fine ground bourbon vanilla provide this natural chocolate with an excellent taste. The chocolate gets its characteristic cream colour because of the use of natural cocoa butter. **Established** In 2002, when a business lady and an innovative sheep farmer came up with a new idea: sheep milk chocolate. In partnership with George Hochleitner, a well known baker, the recipe was created and they contacted Josef Manner & Co. (who had been making chocolate from cacao beans since 1890) regarding large scale production. The company's products are free from cow milk, genetically modified ingredients, soy lecithin and gluten. **Interestingly** Lina was the name of the first sheep born on the farm. The owner, linking this name to chocolate, called the brand Choco-Lina. **Made** In the Josef Manner & Co. factory in the 17th district of Vienna.

Non-deodorised white chocolate Made with sheep milk. Blended with vanilla.

●●Sweet ●●Sheep Milk ●●Butter 30% ●Vanilla

Taste Brown sugar; honey; butter; blanched almond. Hint of herb and spice.

29

PURISSIMA 70%
OHNE ZUCKERZUSATZ

Tiroler Edle ✿ ✿ ✿

An ingeniously simple idea with an impressively sophisticated result. A chocolate dedicated to the enjoyment of the purity of only two ingredients: prestigious cocoa and prestigious milk – with absolutely nothing else added. No added sugar, and more remarkably, no sugar substitute. This revolutionary chocolate is recommended to lovers of dark milk chocolate for its fine flavour profile and its sensitive gentle sweetness from great milk notes. Expect a spectacular pure taste: deliciously dark, yet incredibly creamy. The chocolate's texture is super-fine and it releases complex roast flavours starring delicate nuances of roast nut, yeast, and tobacco. **Tiroler Edle say** 70% cacao, 30% milk and nothing else! No added sugar. Only the natural milk sugar (lactose 7%) included. Forest fruit flavours, tobacco and wood. **Cacao** Carenero Superior, a trinitario variety from Venezuela's central region. **Made At** Konditorei Haag in Landeck, Austria, with exclusive chocolate made by Domori in Italy. **Established** In 2001 by agricultural economist Therese Fiegl (right) who launched an initiative to take the milk and cream of Tyrolean Grey cows and make an extraordinary chocolate with it. Her idea ignited the enthusiasm of Domori and of Hansjörg Haag of Landeck (pictured) a master confectioner who had studied the art of crafting chocolate in Switzerland. "The exquisite milk of the loveable Tyrolean Greys," says Therese, "melts perfectly with high quality cacao. When you combine the very best ingredients with craftsmanship of perfection, you provide a unique joy that sweetens your day and the certainty of having awakened a new awareness for small-scale food production."

Milk chocolate No added sugar or sugar substitute.

●●●Cocoa 70%   ●●Milk 30%   ●●Butter
●●Bitter ●Sweet

Taste Cream; charred wholemeal toast; tobacco; roast hazelnut; roast chestnut. Hint of smoke, tahini and yeast.

WORLD CHOCOLATE AWARDS

WWW.TIROLEREDLE.AT

TIROLER EDLE

ICH WILL SCHOKOLADE

31

PURISSIMA 48% OHNE ZUCKERZUSATZ

Tiroler Edle ✷✷

An elegant revelation of pure, fine, complex, cocoa and milk. Despite having no added sugar, it is complete. A mild and delicate sweetness emerges from the wide range of creamy milk notes that round off the tasty, tender, cocoa. **Tiroler Edle say** Aromas of forest fruits, tobacco, wood and grey cow milk. **Cacao** Carenero Superior. A trinitario variety from Venezuela's central region. **Interestingly** The world's first milk chocolate bar was made in 1875 in Vevey, Switzerland, by Daniel Peter with the help of his friend and neighbour, Henri Nestlé. It had taken Peter eight years to perfect the process. He was by no means the first to try, but all previous attempts to use milk failed because its high water content meant it soon turned rancid. His groundbreaking milk chocolate bar named Gala Peter, after the Greek word for milk, became an international sensation. It made D. Peter one of the world's largest chocolate makers and helped Alpine farmers by increasing demand for milk. Henri Nestlé was a German pharmacist who had immigrated to Switzerland. He founded Nestlé in 1867, using condensed milk to create one of the first infant foods as an alternative for mothers who could not breastfeed their babies. Daniel Peter was a candle maker, but the advent of the kerosene lamp and his marriage to a daughter of local chocolatier François-Louis Cailler inspired him to transform his candle factory in 1867 to found D. Peter chocolate.

Milk chocolate No added sugar or sugar substitute.

●●●Milk 52% ●●Cocoa 48% ●●Butter ●Bitter ●Sweet

Taste Cream; whole milk; chocolate mousse; peanut; wholemeal toast; tobacco. Hint of honey; tahini; dried fruit; salt and yeast.

PURISSIMA 48%

Tiroler Edle ⊗

It's all about the expansive tender notes of mountain milk, paired with sweet, but gentle, chocolate. It develops delightful rounded chocolaty tones as it melts, with no bitterness. Pause and you can sense hints of honey and caramelised nuts, topped generously with rich cream. **Tiroler Edle say** Flavours of peanuts, ripe fruits, tobacco, grey cow milk and sugar. **Cacao** Trinitario, Rio Caribe Superior, from Hacienda San José, Venezuela. **Interestingly** "Superior" does not refer to a variety of cacao, but the grade Hacienda San José give to batches of beans with low defects. To qualify as Superior a minimum of 80% of the beans inspected must be well fermented. Because of this, the beans graded Superior command the highest price. Several countries have national standards for grading beans, in others the particulars vary between producers.

Milk chocolate.

●●●Milk   ●●Sweet   ●●Cocoa 48%
●●Butter

Taste Whole milk; cream; caramel; chocolate mousse; Brazil nut; tobacco; peanut butter cups; honey; maple syrup; cinnamon.

PURISSIMA 75%

Tiroler Edle ⊗

Lovers of dark chocolate will feel at ease with this level of cocoa in the taste, but the creamy milk is definitely there, rounding things off nicely. Unobtrusive sweetness keeps the focus on the refined hues of cacao and the milk's qualities. Think of it as a prestigious dark chocolate, with milk. **Tiroler Edle say** Notes of ripe fruit, peanut and tobacco. **Cacao** Rio Caribe Superior (trinitario) from Hacienda San José, Venezuela. **Interestingly** The milk for Tiroler Edle comes from Tyrolean Greys, a breed of cattle which has grazed the mountains of Tirol for more than three thousand years. Nowadays, they are bred by only a handful of devoted mountain farmers. The cows, fondly nicknamed "noble ones" by the farmers, spend their summers on Tirol's high alpine pastures, where they feast to their heart's content on an incomparable panoply of wild flowers, grasses and herbs which help to make the milk so special. In order to produce the Purissima range of chocolates, one or two trips are arranged each year to collect between 10,000 and 15,000 litres of grey cow milk from the mountainside farms. It is taken to Styria in eastern Austria, where it is dried into a fine milk powder. After being filtered, the milk passes into a tank which has a partial vacuum, which enables a third of its water to be evaporated at a much lower boiling point than normal. During the evaporation process the milk is flash pasteurised at a high temperature for only a few seconds, before being force-cooled. Inside the top of a 20ft wide, 100ft tall "drying tower" the condensed milk is sprayed as a fine mist into 200°C swirling air. The flowing air rapidly removes the water from the drops, leaving dust size milk particles which fall through the cooler air below and into a funnel shaped hopper ready to be packed. It takes approximately 10 litres of Tiroler Edle milk to produce 1kg of milk powder, which is sent to Domori in Italy to be used in making this exclusive range. The modern industrial process of drying milk is centred on preserving its original flavour profile by avoiding the high temperatures that cause a spoilt milk taste. This has only been possible for the last century and a half, and at first was a closely guarded secret. The earliest record of milk being dried was written by Marco Polo seven hundred years ago. He observed that the Mongolians dried milk to use it on their travels. It was made by skimming the top off boiling milk (it was necessary to remove this part, but it was also used for butter) and setting out the remainder in the sun to dry. The slightly acidic paste could then be mixed with water when needed. "In the morning a man will put a quarter of a kilo of it into his leather bottle, and as much water as he pleases. As he rides his horse, the two will get well churned together into a kind of liquid that he makes his dinner," Polo wrote.

Milk chocolate.

●●●Cocoa 75% ●●Milk ●●Butter ●●Bitter ●Sweet

Taste Tahini; peanut; Brazil nut; whole milk; cream; tobacco; leather; charred wholemeal toast; treacle. Hint of coffee, mushroom, honey and smoke.

ERDBEER KOKOS

Mitzi Blue by Zotter ✣

Here we have mellow, creamy, chocolate, accentuated by dreamy hints of coconut. But the zesty strawberry livens things up and tempers the bold sweetness. The result is a scrumptious pink chocolate. **Zotter say** Seductive and elegant at the same time. A special, unique taste. **Established** In 1999 by Josef Zotter, who had made chocolates and pastries since 1992. In 2007 Zotter opened a complete chocolate factory: the only one in Europe to work from the cacao beans to finished bar exclusively using organic and fair trade standards. **Made** In Riegersburg, South East of Graz, Austria. **Interestingly** Each year more than one hundred and fifty thousand people experience the factory's guided tasting tours. Right: roasted beans are shelled in a five deck winnowing system.

White chocolate Blended with vanilla, strawberry and coconut.

●●●Strawberry ●●●Sweet
●●●Milk ●●Butter 34%
●Coconut ●Vanilla ●Sour

Taste Cream; coconut; lemon; strawberry; icing sugar; honey.

KUVERTÜRE

Basic Dunkle Bergmilch
Zotter ⊗ ⊗

This would be an easy first step to take for a light milk chocolate lover who would like a bit more ommph. "Dark Mountain Milk" lives up to its name, providing plenty of mid-range cocoa notes to enjoy, rounded off by exceptional milk. Salt has been used sparingly: just to encourage the cocoa, which is evidently a careful blend of quality varieties. **Zotter say** Full chocolate indulgence with a disproportionately high cocoa content of 50% offers a chocolate enjoyment with a delicate milk flavour. With naturally pure mountain milk from the Tyrol farmers, pure cocoa butter, natural sugar and genuine vanilla. **Interestingly** Zotter not only ensure that all of their raw product suppliers are organic and Fairtrade, they are also a family business. Josef and Ulrike Zotter are delighted that their daughter Julia is already working on cacao-related research in Brazil, and son Michael is studying food technology.

Milk chocolate Blended with a trace of salt.

●●●Cocoa 50%　　●●Milk　　●●Butter
●●Sweet　●Salt　●Vanilla　●Bitter

Taste　Cream; dark caramel; hazelnut; sultana. Hint of salt and spice.

Zotter Cacaofèvier www.zotter.at

41

NICARAGUA
Zotter ✶ ✶

The best way to describe Nicaragua is to point out that it is one of few milk chocolates in which cocoa mass is the principal ingredient. This ultra-dark milk chocolate's rich roasted cacao flavours are rounded off with a drop of milk and caramel. An imperceptible pinch of salt and vanilla have been used to enhance the cocoa notes. Expect a dry finish. **Zotter say** Wow - around 60% cocoa content in a milk chocolate - this is something really special. The cocoa is accompanied by a light sweetness of natural sugar. Chocolates with a high cocoa content require a high-quality cocoa. With his seventy seven years, Don Francisco possesses plenty of knowledge and wisdom with regard to growing cacao. **Cacao** From La Cruz del Río Grande, Nicaragua. **Interestingly** Every year Zotter use 460 tons of cocoa; 160 tons of sugar from Paraguay; and a million litres of milk from Austria's Tyrol mountains.

Milk chocolate Blended with vanilla and a trace of salt.

●●●Cocoa 60% ●Milk ●Butter ●Sweet ●Bitter

Taste Charred wholemeal toast; butter; black pepper; molasses. Hint of caramel and cream.

ZOTTER CACAOFÈVIER WWW.ZOTTER.AT

BELGIUM

JASMINE TEA & VIOLET EXTRACTS

Café-Tasse ✤

An exciting, tantalising treat for the taste buds. This is an original and perfect match: dreamy waves of violet and vivacious, crunchy jasmine flower have been swirled into a sweet, yet substantial chocolate. **Café-Tasse say** It is as tasty and rich in cocoa content as it is creative in its taste associations. With this flavour of far away places on your lips, you can taste the aroma of the tropics and the magical world of aromatic essences. **Established** Twenty years ago in Brussels, Café-Tasse remains a family-owned and run business. **Made** In Belgium. **Interestingly** Thomas Moore wrote a poem about jasmine (left) which is known in India as the "Queen of the Night."

T'was midnight-through the lattice wreath'd
With woodbine, many a perfume breath'd
From plants that wake while others sleep,
From timid jasmine buds, that keep
Their odour to themselves all day,
But when the sunshine dies away,
Let the delicious secret out
To every breeze that roams about.

Milk chocolate Blended with violet oil. Containing jasmine leafs.

●●●Sweet ●●Violet ●●Jasmine ●●Cocoa 40% ●●Milk ●●Butter

Taste Dry jasmine; violet; cream; honey; chocolate mousse; caramel. Hint of hazelnut and coffee.

LAIT NOUGATINE

Dolfin ✿

Honey-sweet, with irresistible light flavours of cocoa and nut to play on the tongue, plus delightful fine texture. **Dolfin say** Nougat milk chocolate evokes memories of childhood sweets. A crunchy, delicate concoction. A piece of chocolate at the end of a meal is a well-known tradition but it has been lacking in panache… True to its creative spirit, Dolfin came up with the gourmet squares: a combination of many colourful flavours. The gourmet square is impressive because it is very difficult to make: the slimness of the chocolate means that the choice of ingredients has to be perfect in terms of size and flavour content. Enjoy a square, with something to drink, with a dessert, or just on its own. **Established** In 1989 by brothers Michael and Jean-Francois Poncelet. Perhaps their passion for chocolate was inherited from their parents, who owned Neuhaus at one time. **Made** In Wauthier-Braine, Belgium.

Milk chocolate Blended with vanilla. Containing minute chips of hazelnut and almond nougat.

●●●Sweet ●●Milk ●●Nougat ●Cocoa 32% ●Butter ●Vanilla

Taste Honey; caramel; whole milk. Hint of meringue, hazelnut, cinnamon and almond.

49

ROOIBUSH
Dolfin ✪

Fine shreds of rooibush add texture and vibrant "red" flavours, such as aniseed and cherry, to this sweet and tasty chocolate. A superb fusion of two complex and delightful flavours, both highly prized by their respective original native cultures. **Dolfin say** When the winter snow covers the ground, rooibush will warm the heart. Delightful round and slightly caramelised chocolate flavours. **Interestingly** Rooibush (also known as redbush) is indigenous to, and exclusive to, South Africa's Cederberg mountain range (pictured). Its flower is bright yellow and instead of leaves it has green needles that turn deep red when dried. They are naturally quite sweet, and without bitterness. Rooibush is widely available as a tea.

Milk chocolate Containing minute strands of dried rooibush plant.

●●●Sweet ●●Milk ●●Cocoa 32% ●Rooibush ●Butter ●Vanilla

Taste Sweet cherry; root beer; ginger; aniseed; caramel; butter; vanilla; cream; chocolate; black pepper.

Hot Masala

Dolfin

It's not hot, it's warm and friendly. Creamy cinnamon and ginger are complimented by gentle, warm spices. **Dolfin say** Originally from India, hot masala is a mixture of colourful spices that are invigorating in winter and refreshing in summer. Usually taken in tea with milk, once added to chocolate, hot masala is a wonderful surprise containing new and comforting flavours. **Interestingly** Masala is a Hindi word meaning a dry mixture of ground spices. In India the ingredients of masala vary from household to household.

Milk chocolate Blended with vanilla and warm spices.

●●●Sweet ●●●Cinnamon
●●●Milk ●●Hot ●●Cocoa 32%
●Butter ●Vanilla

Taste Cinnamon; ginger; black pepper; clove; cardamom; warm spice; caramel; milk; condensed milk; vanilla.

COCOA BEANS FROM GHANA

Dolfin ✢

Attention-grabbing caramelised chocolate tones mingle and contrast with hearty cocoa nib flavours creating a spectacle of light and darkness in this sweet, but flavoursome, bar. **Dolfin say** An African melody, a little raw, but welcoming. The milk chocolate brings roundness and a sense of greater intimacy. **Interestingly** In 1815 Dutch missionaries planted cacao in Ghana, but it was when local farmer Tetteh Quarshie brought seeds from the island of Fernando Po, off Cameroon, in 1879 that cultivation became widespread and the nation's economy transformed. Until then, palm oil and rubber were the main industries. In 1886 the Governor had more cacao beans brought from São Tomé to boost production and Ghana now produces 700,000 tonnes of cacao annually.

Milk chocolate Blended with vanilla. Containing minute cocoa nibs.

●●●Sweet ●●Milk ●●Cocoa 32% ●●Butter ●●Vanilla

Taste Cream; fresh ginger; cinnamon; caramel; salted butter; vanilla; freshly ground black pepper; deep roasted cocoa nibs. Hint of nut.

55

Pistaches d'Evoïa Grillées Salées

Laurent Gerbaud ✕ ✕ ✕

A highly refined chocolate with understated power, done justice with the finest pistachios. The tender flavours mingle harmoniously, until eventually the cocoa reigns supreme. And so the experience is brought to pleasing, flavoursome finish. **Laurent says** Exceptional sweetness and softness. A touch of Guérande salt and roasted and salted Evoïa pistachios complete this subtle picture. It really provokes addiction: when you start, you eat one and you cannot stop! **Cacao** Nacional from Ecuador. **Made** In The workshop and shop in Brussels, using an exclusive chocolate made from the beans by Domori, Italy. **Pictured** A dried cacao pod sits in front of Gerbaud's "Little Bit of Everything" selection box.

Milk Chocolate Blended with salt, scattered with salted whole pistachios.

●●●Milk ●●Cocoa 50% ●●Pistachio ●●Butter ●Sweet ●Salt ●Bitter

Taste Whipped cream; whole milk; butter; cocoa dust; fresh grass; grapefruit; dark cherry; white wine; malt; almond; roast; coffee; salt; dark wood smoke; light caramel; pistachio.

LAURENT GERBAUD · WWW.CHOCOLATSGERBAUD.BE

57

CHOCOLAT AU LAIT

Laurent Gerbaud ⊗ ⊗ ⊗

A kaleidoscope of dairy notes accompany base-to-medium chocolate notes, exhibiting powerful cocoa in the most elegant way conceivable. This is a smooth, finely balanced chocolate, rich in tastes to explore and admire. Patience is rewarded: the flavours just keep on coming, next releasing notes from higher ranges. **Laurent Gerbaud says** The milk chocolate designed by Domori for Laurent Gerbaud is a mix of rare nacional beans from Ecuador. It has exceptional sweetness and softness. A touch of Guérande salt completes this subtle picture. Domori, one of the best luxury chocolate makers in Europe, works only with the best cocoa beans in very small quantities, using a manufacturing process that allows the expression of all aromas of the chocolate. This philosophy met exactly Laurent Gerbaud's own objectives, and so began a very nice partnership. **Cacao** Nacional from Ecuador. **Interestingly** The Gerbaud logo is a red seal that features the word "chocolate" in Chinese. It represents discovery and the exotic tastes from far-away lands that often inspire this creative chocolatier who spent some years in China. He became impressed how "they were not using any sugar in the cuisine. After the trip I stopped using sugar [in dark chocolates] which means I got interested in all the other tastes."

Milk chocolate Blended with salt.

●●●Milk ●●Cocoa 50% ●●Butter ●●Sweet ●Salt ●Bitter

Taste Whipped cream; butter; cocoa dust; fresh green grass; roast; grapefruit; dark cherry; white wine; malt; almond; coffee; salt; dark wood; smoke.

LAURENT GERBAUD WWW.CHOCOLATSGERBAUD.BE

Noisettes du Piémont Grillées Caramélisées

Laurent Gerbaud ✷ ✷

Precious cocoa with long, long milky tones. The crisp roasted hazelnuts from northern Italy, and their slight coating of caramelised sugar, are as delicate as the first-class chocolate. Immensely enjoyable to crunch and munch superficially, but this subtle composition takes time to release all of its cocoa nuances. **Laurent says** A hint of salt, a touch of sugar, a refined harmony for our voluptuous milk chocolate. The soft chocolate, the Guérande salt, the grilled and caramelised hazelnuts form an addictive blend, bite after bite. It is a temptation you cannot resist... **Cacao** Nacional from Ecuador. **Interestingly** The Gerbaud chocolate shop is located in the historical centre of Brussels. It features large windows into the workshop so that visitors may see the chocolates being created. There is a bar from which his special blend of thick hot chocolate is served. **Pictured** Left: the bags on display contain a speciality of the house, meticulously selected varieties of citrus fruit, Corsican prunes, Guilin ginger and Izmir figs coated in the finest chocolate.

Milk Chocolate Blended with salt. Scattered on one side with grilled and caramelised whole hazelnuts.

●●●Milk ●●Cocoa 50% ●●Hazelnut ●●Butter ●Caramel ●Sweet ●Salt ●Bitter

Taste Whipped cream; whole milk; butter; cocoa dust; fresh grass; grapefruit; dark cherry; white wine; malt; almond; roast; coffee; salt; dark wood smoke; light caramel; roasted hazelnut.

Laurent Gerbaud www.chocolatsgerbaud.be

CHOCOLAT AU LAIT

Pierre Marcolini ⊗ ⊗

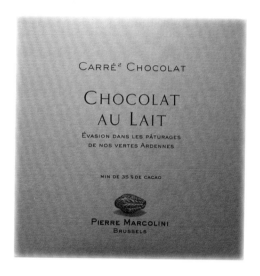

An elegant and sensual homage to classic milk chocolate: long luxurious waves of buttery cocoa and aromatic vanilla are lightened by fabulously fresh-tasting milk. The chocolate is enriched by graceful caramel, roast and nut qualities. **Marcolini say** Escape to the green pastures of the Ardennes. Creamy milk chocolate with a subtle caramel note. **Established** In 1995 in Brussels by Pierre Marcolini. When he was a boy Pierre decided to become a pastry chef. By nineteen he achieved this, under the guidance of François Foulon, studying at the Ceria university in Brussels. All of his talents, from ice cream making, to chocolate, to confectionary and cake, were employed at the Parisienne in Brussels. In the millennium Pierre decided on a new challenge: to make chocolate starting with the beans. He began to import cacao the very next year, becoming the only chocolatier in Belgium to make his own chocolate. **Made** In Haren, Brussels. **Pictured** On their arrival, the jute sacks of beans are stored next-door to the roasting room. Top right: roasted beans are emptied into a tray below the oven, where they are turned by rotating rakes to halt the roast with cool air.

Milk chocolate Blended with vanilla and a trace of salt.

●●●Butter ●●●Milk ●●●Vanilla ●●Cocoa 35% ●●Sweet ●Salt

Taste Fresh whole milk; chocolate; Brazil nut; light caramel; earth; flower; roast. Hint of coffee and salt.

Plaisir Five O'Clock

Pierre Marcolini ✵ ✵ ✵

As your teeth break the brittle amber caramel, sensational roasted pistachio, hazelnut and almond flavours flourish. There are assorted textures: smooth, tender, chewy and crunchy. To top it off, the soft rich chocolate it was encased in starts to melt and delight. This is a harmony of the finest flavours. **Pierre Marcolini says** Milk chocolate with pralinated Faro almonds and old-style nougatine. A little snack to slip into your pocket. **Interestingly** Here, Pierre (pictured) has combined his expertise with chocolate and his skills as a master pastry chef which gained him the honour of winning the 1995 "Coupe du Monde de la Pâtisserie" in Lyon.

Milk chocolate Blended with vanilla. Containing a layer of caramel brittle with finely chopped pieces of almond, pistachio and hazelnut nougat.

●●●Cocoa 50% ●●Milk ●●Caramel ●●Nougat ●●Butter ●●Sweet ●Vanilla

Taste Nougat; pistachio; hazelnut; almond; flower; vanilla; roast; butter; caramel brittle. Hint of salt.

JAVA LAIT

Pierre Marcolini ⊗ ⊗

Here is a chocolate with a clean, full taste of fresh milk, alongside long-lasting caramel and butter notes. It's a mellow chocolate: rounded and gentle, underscored by a variety of savoury and sweet flavours. The soothing experience concludes with a roasted aftertaste. **Marcolini say** All the delicateness of Indonesia. Slightly acidic red berry notes, wonderful freshness. **Cacao** From the volcanic island of Java, Indonesia. **Interestingly** There are two Pierre Marcolini shops situated in Brussels' Place du Grand Sablon. A grand boutique (pictured) and the other a compact "Manufacture" store with an open kitchen where the cakes, macaroons and such are made in front of your eyes. The macaroon to try is violet, covered in dark chocolate. There is also a rather special delicately spiced hot chocolate. And then there are the biscuits…

Milk chocolate Blended with vanilla and a trace of salt.

●●●Butter ●●Cocoa 50% ●●Milk ●●Sweet ●●Vanilla

Taste Latte; mascarpone; cinnamon; orange; flower; honey; candied cherry; hazelnut; butter; malt. Hint of yeast and smoke.

PIERRE MARCOLINI CACAOFÉVIER WWW.MARCOLINI.BE

Sans Sucres Ajoutés

Pierre Marcolini �

Drift away... Sensual buttery cocoa, heavenly cream and soft notes of caramel make this bar very easy to enjoy. Delicate sweetness, vanilla and salt have been used subtly to enhance this dreamy chocolate experience. **Pierre Marcolini says** Deliciously caramelised. All the pleasure of milk chocolate, without the guilt, ideal for diabetics and people on a sugar free diet. Maltitol is the substitute for the sweet taste. It gives a good chocolaty texture and keeps calories down. **Cacao** A blend of nacional from the Los Rios region of Ecuador and forastero from Ghana. **Interestingly** Pierre Marcolini released this chocolate in February of 2010. It is made with SweetPearl, a maltitol sweetener from the Roquette company in France. The white crystalline powder, obtained from cereals such as corn and wheat, has nearly half the calories of sugar. "SweetPearl leaves room for the cocoa bean and its flavour from the roasting." remarked Pierre at its launch. "For us it's inspiring that there are new products on the market that provide sweetness for chocolate lovers for them not to feel guilty about indulging and savouring their favourite treat." **Pictured** Wrapping hand made caramels.

Milk chocolate No added sugar. Sweetened with maltitol. Blended with vanilla and a trace of salt.

●●●Butter   ●●Cocoa 50%   ●●Milk   ●Sweet
●Vanilla

Taste Chocolate; light caramel; cream; roast; honeydew melon; malt; butter. Hint of roast chestnut, hazelnut and salt.

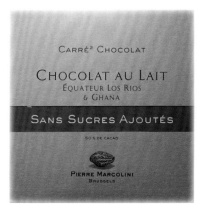

World Chocolate Awards · Pierre Marcolini · Cacao Février · www.marcolini.be

CHOCOLAT BLANC

Pierre Marcolini ✦ ✦ ✦

A duet of divine sweet cream and highly aromatic fresh cuttings of vanilla pod, which speckle the chocolate. The complexity of the orchid's sweet, faintly spicy, fragrance is enhanced by sweet golden honey flavours. This "grand vanilla" chocolate showcases the qualities of one of the world's favourite ingredients in a way that has not been done before. **Pierre Marcolini says** A gentle stroll back to childhood memories. Pure cocoa butter with fresh Tahitian vanilla and superior milk powder. **Interestingly** The vanilla tahitensis orchid (Tahitian vanilla) is the rarest of the two species of vanilla used to flavour food. It represents only 5% of the world market, with bourbon (planifolia) vanilla making up the remainder. Brought from Guatemala, via the Philippines, to Tahiti, Tahitian is a hybrid of bourbon and odorata vanilla. Both parents grow naturally only in Central America, but Tahitian has never been discovered growing wild. Botanists believe that the hybrid occurred when the parent species were planted together by the Mayas.

White chocolate Blended with vanilla and a trace of salt.

●●●Vanilla ●●Butter ●●Sweet ●●Milk

Taste Cream; honey; flower; custard. Hint of salt and anise.

PLAISIR BREAKFAST
Pierre Marcolini ⊗ ⊗

A graceful harmony of three fine, tender, flavours and textures. The minute pieces of aromatic candied orange and tasty puffed rice merge seamlessly with the elegant chocolate, making a delightful sensual delicacy. **Marcolini say** Milk chocolate with orange zests and crisp puffed rice. A fragrant tablet with a remarkable balance of smooth and crunchy, for all tastes. **Pictured Below:** Yan Pennor's designs for Pierre Marcolini include the iconic square (yet rounded) chocolate tablet. "You have the impression that you are looking at a wooden object; you may imagine that it's the well-known letter game where you have to move the letters around; but actually it's a bar of chocolate. And we are lucky that we have a nine letter name!" Pierre observed.

Milk chocolate Blended with vanilla. Containing minute pieces of crisp puffed rice and candied orange zest.

●●Cocoa 50% ●●Sweet   ●●Butter   ●●Orange
●●Rice   ●Vanilla

Taste Lightly candied orange peel; cappuccino; cinnamon; honey; hazelnut; cream; quinoa; butter; malt; roast. Hint of nut.

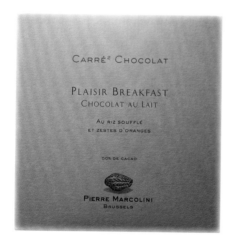

BELIZE

DARK MILK
Cotton Tree Chocolate ⊛ ⊛

A gentle giant. This truly dark milk chocolate will hold your interest as it reveals a delicious array of intriguing cola and dry roasted notes, rounded with butter and a refreshing drop of milk. Expect a satisfyingly deep roasted aftertaste. **Cotton Tree Chocolate say** What is most important is that we are able to pick the very best beans as we are only one block away from the Toledo Cacao Growers Association co-operative. We don't blend our beans, so our bars have different flavours all the time. Tobacco, raisin, caramel, toast, tea, bee wax, malt, butter and coffee notes can be found amongst the different batches of Dark Milk. **Made** In Punta Gorda, on the Caribbean coast of Toledo, South Belize. **Cacao** From Toledo. **Established** In April of 2008.

Milk chocolate Blended with vanilla.

●●●Cocoa 55%   ●●Sweet   ●●Butter   ●Milk   ●Vanilla   ●Bitter

Taste Hazelnut; walnut; almond; banana; raisin; green pepper; butter; milk; molasses; coffee; mushroom; cola; cinnamon.

Light Milk with Cocoa Nibs

Cotton Tree Chocolate ✤ ✤ ✤

A generous helping of perfectly roasted "al dente" cocoa nibs have been scattered onto the surface of this flavoursome nutty and buttery chocolate. This spectacular fusion celebrates the richness of cocoa with long-lasting and complex notes, given finesse by the milk and butter. **Cotton Tree Chocolate say** The fact that we make our nib bar in milk chocolate brings out the nuttiness of the nibs, and cuts out any bitterness. We take lots of care with our roasting: we want to taste the cocoa bean, not the roast. **Cacao** From Toledo, Belize. **Interestingly** When asked about the uncommon medium brown colour of the cocoa nibs, Juli Puryear at Cotton Tree explained, "We roast beans for twenty to twenty three minutes, depending upon their moisture content. We roast in small batches, which allows us to exercise good quality control. I believe this has a huge impact on the flavour and quality of our chocolate."

Milk chocolate Blended with vanilla. With cocoa nibs on one side.

●●●Cocoa 46%   ●●Butter   ●●Milk   ●Sweet   ●Vanilla   ●Bitter

Taste Hazelnut; walnut; roast chestnut; almond; olive; cream; caramel; roast; molasses; coffee. Hint of cinnamon, cola and black pepper.

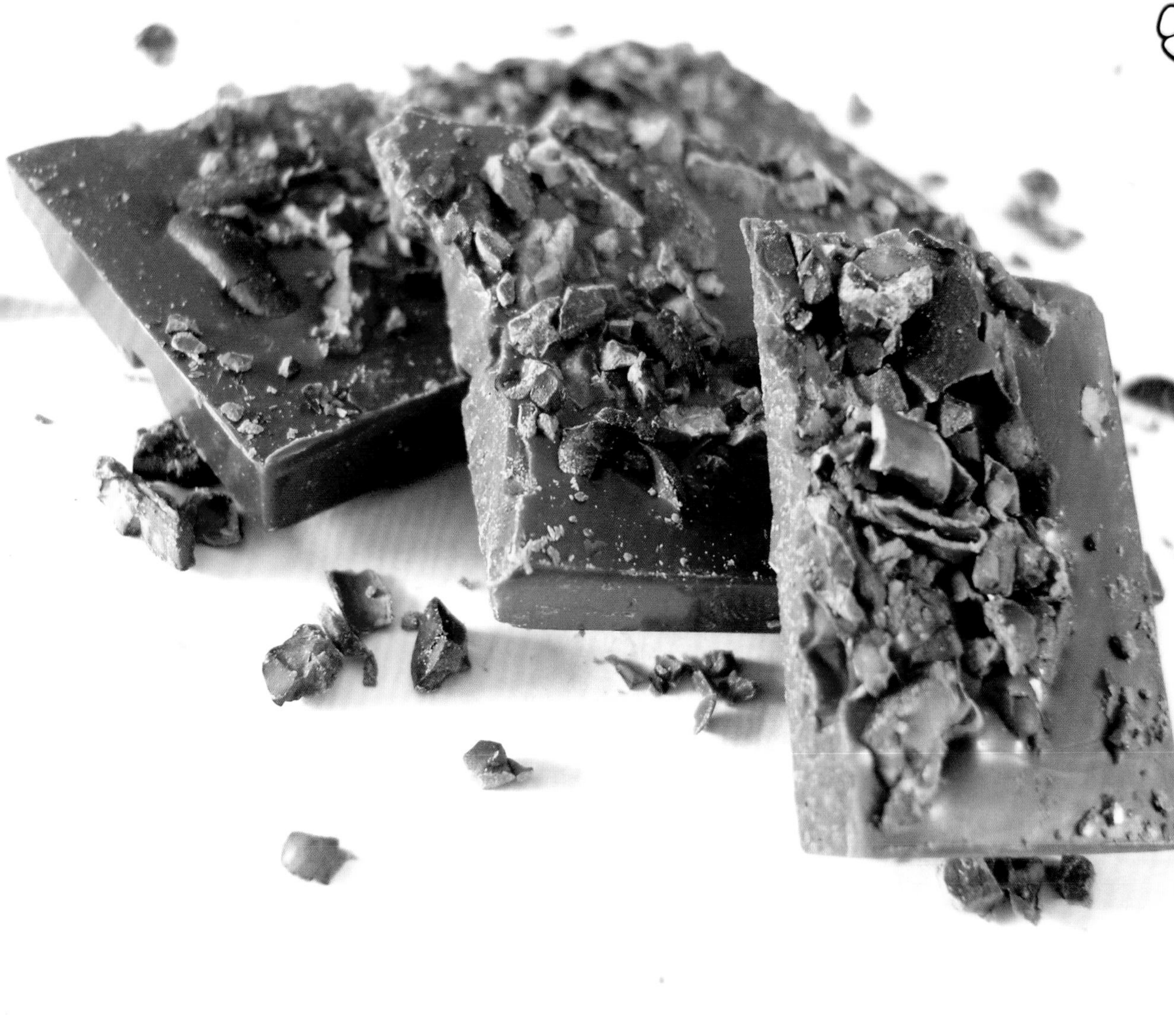

LIGHT MILK

Cotton Tree Chocolate ⊗ ⊗

Relaxing and moreish because of its harmony of lingering nutty and buttery flavours, "Light Milk" has numerous rare and tasteful notes to savour. **Cotton Tree Chocolate say** More than just single origin, each batch of our chocolate starts with cocoa beans from a single day's harvest, from a single farmer. The light milk has cream, caramel, vanilla and cinnamon notes. On several occasions we have had a batch that smelled like buttered popcorn! **Cacao** From Toledo, Belize. **Interestingly** Cotton Tree use organic cacao grown by the surrounding Kekchi and Mopan Mayan villagers. Ruins in the region, some even in the cacao plantations, are evidence that for hundreds of years Belize was heavily populated by the Maya, whose relatively advanced civilisation reached its height between 250 and 900 AD. Eventually the civilisation declined, leaving behind small groups.

Milk chocolate Blended with vanilla.

●●Cocoa 40%   ●●Sweet   ●●Butter   ●●Milk   ●Vanilla

Taste Hazelnut; walnut; almond; butter; cream; olive; malt; sugar cane. Hint of molasses, fruit, coffee and cinnamon.

WHITE WITH VANILLA BEAN

Goss Chocolate ✿ ✿ ✿

Indulge your senses with one of the world's most flavoursome white chocolates. The exceptional floral qualities of the vanilla can be appreciated in harmony with the sweet, fragrant and nutty nuances of a special and pure cocoa butter. **Goss say** We make our own cocoa butter from the same organic beans as our chocolate. They are selected for flavour and carefully roasted in small batches. We do not deodorise it - it is fresh and aromatic. **Cacao** Organic, from Toledo, Belize. **Established** In 2007 by Kerry Goss, who had been making chocolate for friends and family since 2005. **Made** At the Blue Crab Resort, Seine Bight Village, Placencia, Toledo. **Interestingly** Goss not only use locally grown cacao, they also use Belizean cane sugar and vanilla to make this speckled chocolate. Goss are one of very few cacaofèviers in the world who extract their own cocoa butter to make white chocolate. "We make cocoa butter on a very small scale by hand. Select beans are carefully roasted then winnowed and ground to fine liqueur in stone melanguers. The liqueur is pressed in a hand-made press with heat and a twenty tonne jack that is hand cranked. The cocoa cake is reserved behind a cloth filter and the cocoa butter runs out." Kerry explained. **Pictured** In Toledo, many Maya prepare chocolate in a similar way to their ancestors. Sun dried unfermented cacao beans are turned to ensure an even roast on top of a clay or metal plate over a fire. Next, the hot beans are crushed with a stone and put into a basket or bowl so that they can be tossed in the air. This process, called winnowing, separates the cocoa nib from the unwanted shell, which blows away because it is lighter. The nibs are ground into chocolate paste between the volcanic stone of a metate and its hand held scraper. The paste is whisked with hot water in a jug, then poured into cups to drink. The recipe depends on the preference of the drinker: some prefer it strong, others like a larger proportion of water. It is drunk straight, or with a pinch of allspice or chilli, which is prepared in the same way: sun dried, roasted and ground. Vanilla or stingless bee honey is sometimes used. Cinnamon, nutmeg, sugar, orange, almond and milk are not native ingredients, they were introduced by Europeans.

Non-deodorised white chocolate Blended with vanilla.

●●Vanilla   ●●Sweet   ●●Milk   ●●Butter 45%

Taste Salted butter; vanilla; custard; cream; lavender honey; rape honey; cashew; peanut.

LIGHT MILK

IXCACAO Maya Belizean Chocolate ⊗ ⊗

Almost-dark (three percent milk) chocolate, bursting with lingering fruity, citrus and nutty flavours. This robust chocolate is so rich in roasted cacao that it is a meal in itself. As you savour the astounding flavours the slight texture serves as a pleasant reminder that it is home made. **IXCACAO say** This is chocolate like you've probably never tasted before, with an intense flavour. **Cacao** Cultivated organically in the surrounding countryside. **Established** In 1985 as Cyrila's (after Juan's mother) the name was changed on the 21st of December 2012 to mark the transition to a new era of the Maya calendar. **Made** In San Felipe village, near Punta Gorda, Toledo, South Belize. **Interestingly** IXCACAO is the world's only Maya tree-to-bar chocolatier. In an unspoilt region of Belize, Abelina Cho creates chocolate at home from the cacao her husband Juan cultivates on the land inherited from his father.

Milk chocolate Blended with vanilla.

●●●Cocoa 65%   ●●Sweet   ●●Milk 3%   ●●Butter   ●Bitter

Taste Grapefruit; balsamic vinegar; brownie; banana; strawberry; nut; black pepper; allspice. Hint of milk.

got chocolate?

Authentic Mayan Chocolate Making

Cyrila's *Chocolates*

DAILY TOURS ·
Organic Farm Tours starting at 9:00AM
Chocolate Making Demonstration
11:30AM, 1:00PM & by appointment
Authentic Mayan Lunch & Dinner

501-742-4050

www.ecomayachocolate.com

BRAZIL

Leave behind any preconceptions of how a 30% milk chocolate should taste. Here is a concentration and intensity of rare flavours that will impress dark milk chocolate connoisseurs. The milk is mild. Persistent, wholesome, cocoa notes flourish with each second that passes. **Amma say** A classic lush and velvety milk chocolate made with a blend of cacao that creates a harmonious rich milk chocolate experience. **Cacao** Forastero: amelonado strain. There are subvarieties such as Pará and Porto Seguro, but Parazinho is the most prevalent. From the Atlantic Rainforest, South Bahia, Brazil. **Made** In Salvador, Bahia, Brazil. **Established** In 2007. Amma is a partnership between American Frederick Schilling, who founded Dagoba chocolate in 2001, and Brazilian Diego Badaró, who owns several organic cacao plantations in the rainforests of the Bahia region. In 2007 Frederick received a mysterious box of cacao bean samples sent by a man called Diego in Brazil. The beans were of such high quality, that a month later Frederick was on a plane to meet Diego and they immediately realised that their journey together had only just begun. This meeting, initiated by one hundred little beans, gave birth to Amma chocolate. Because they produce chocolate in the same region in which the cacao is grown and own their own farms, Amma are able to gain deep insight into, and interact in, every step of the tree to bar process.

Milk chocolate.

●●●Cocoa 30% ●Milk ●Sweet ●Bitter

Taste Marzipan; treacle; carrot; radish; dark raisin; orange marmalade.

30%
Amma ✿✿✿

WWW.AMMACHOCOLATE.COM

AMMA CHOCOLATE · CACAOFEVIER

45%
Amma ✦✦

An impressive and curious array of great notes that will stir the emotions of any cocoa enthusiast. A chocolate with a long lasting taste and a slightly dry finish. **Amma say** This contemporary chocolate is super creamy, with slight touches of floral notes. It is a "milk" with a full flavour of cocoa that will impress the lovers of stronger chocolate. **Cacao** Forastero: amelonado strain. Sub varieties include Pará, and Porto Seguro, but Parazinho is the most prevalent. From the Atlantic Rainforest, South Bahia, Brazil. **Interestingly** It was in 1736 that Frenchman Louis Frederic Warneaux introduced cacao to the Bahia region. It was at the time when the once great sugar cane plantations there had started to decline due to the falling prices in Europe. Warneaux literally planted the seeds for a cacao boom which brought prosperity to Bahia's land owners a century later, thanks to soaring demand for chocolate in Europe. **Pictured** Fermentation is carried out in wood barrels with the beans covered. Long sticks with sharp hooks are used to harvest cacao pods from the branches and trunks of taller trees.

Milk chocolate.

●●●Cocoa 45% ●●Sweet ●Milk ●Butter ●Bitter

Taste Vanilla fudge; strawberry jam; chocolate brownie; malt; almond; milk.

BAHIA · BRAZIL

60 KG

ECUADOR

FINE MILK CHOCOLATE

Caoni ✿✿

This caramelised chocolate carries many fine nutty and floral flavours. They are slowly released as it melts, developing into a crescendo of colourful sweet and sophisticated notes. **Caoni say** Just like our dark chocolate, we produce our milk chocolate with one hundred percent arriba cocoa beans. You can truly savour every bite of our chocolate without the taste of flavourings such as vanilla, usually present in most milk chocolates. **Cacao** Nacional from Ecuador. **Established** In 2005. **Made** From the beans by Tulicorp in Guayaquil, Ecuador, for Caoni. **Pictured** San Rafael, Ecuador's largest falls, in the Amazon region. Right: Selections of Caoni's chocolate bars are available in wooden gift boxes.

Milk chocolate.

●●●Sweet ●●Milk ●●Butter ●●Cocoa 35%

Taste Strawberry; red bell pepper; cheese; flower; honey; black pepper; salt; toffee; banana; nut; long life milk; double cream.

CAONI WWW.CAONICHOCOLATE.COM

MACADAMIA

Caoni ✿ ✿

Caoni's remarkably nutty, floral, lightly caramelised chocolate is particularly suited to this careful addition of macadamia. A laid-back harmony of long-lasting flavours. **Caoni say** Specially selected and toasted in the proprietary method, the macadamia nuts have given this bar an incredible taste and texture. Only one kilo is selected per every four kilos of macadamia nuts and you will revel in each bite. **Cacao** Nacional from Ecuador. **Interestingly** Caoni take their name from a river which runs down from the Andes into the Ecuadorian rainforest where it helps to irrigate the land of hundreds of native families who use their ancestral knowledge to cultivate cacao. These are the tropical lowlands of Esmeraldas, Manbi and Los Rios.

Milk chocolate With minute chips of roasted macadamia nut.

●●●Sweet ●●Milk ●●Butter ●●Cocoa ●Macadamia

Taste Butter; light caramel; flower; honey; Brazil nut; peanut; macadamia. Hint of vanilla.

CAONI   WWW.CAONICHOCOLATE.COM

97

PASSION FRUIT
Caoni ⊗

Caoni have added passion fruit to their flavoursome chocolate, which has tremendous butter toffee, nut and floral qualities. The minute pieces are evenly distributed and an equilibrium is maintained between the chocolate and fruit throughout. **Caoni say** Caoni's all-natural product combines our milk chocolate with the unique taste of passion fruit. This creates a fabulous explosion of flavours and concludes with a long-lasting sensation of the fruit's tang, balanced against the sweetness of Caoni's milk chocolate. **Cacao** Nacional from Ecuador. **Interestingly** Passion fruit is not from a tree, but a climbing vine.

Milk chocolate With minute pieces of dried passion fruit.

●●●Sweet ●●●Butter ●●Milk
●●Cocoa ●●Passion fruit
●Sour

Taste Wild flower honey; walnut; butter; toffee; passion fruit. Hint of vanilla and herbs.

ENGLAND

Pale Lemon & Sea Salt

Amelia Rope ✿ ✿

Vivid sea salt and mellow lemon oil play together in this rounded, creamy and caramelised chocolate. The result is a moreish treat that constantly engages you. **Amelia says** The addiction of Maldon sea salt and milk chocolate is unbelievable, but put in a smidge of organic lemon oil and suffice to say it has become a bestseller. I think it's delicious with a buttery white wine like Viognier and also champagne too. **Cacao** Nacional from Ecuador. **Established** September of 2007. "Having always been interested in the world of food and cooking I found myself captivated more and more by chocolate and after attending a course at Valrhona in France, 'Les Bonbons de Chocolat,' there was no looking back," Amelia explains. "Immersed in chocolate day and night and living amongst 3kg bags of chocolate pastilles from different geographical origins, and varying cocoa percentages led me to explore further the world of chocolate and guided me to becoming a chocolatier." **Made** In Leigh, Surrey, England.

Milk chocolate Blended with salt and pale lemon oil.

●●●Salt ●●Sweet ●●Milk ●●Butter ●●Cocoa 40% ●Lemon

Taste Caramel; salt; sweet lemon; butter. Hint of nut.

Amelia Rope   www.ameliarope.com

PALE HAZELNUT & SEA SALT

Amelia Rope ✽

Just the perfect proportion of delicious hazelnuts has been scattered into this smooth chocolate which is defined by sweet, caramelised notes and lively salt. **Amelia Rope says** Using the creamy caramel tasting single origin milk chocolate, adding Maldon sea salt and then sprinkling organic roasted hazelnuts on top, it is a treat for the taste buds and, well, I find that not always one chunk is enough, but who knows?! **Cacao** Nacional from Ecuador. **Interestingly** Maldon sea salt has been harvested on the banks of the River Blackwater for over two thousand years. Sea water is taken from the river on the spring tides, when the concentration of salt is highest. It is pumped ashore and held in storage tanks. The water is filtered and then transferred to large steel salt pans, where the boiling process takes place. As the water evaporates, salt crystals form on the surface of the water. As they grow in size and weight they sink to the bottom of the pan. The soft, white, flaky crystals are harvested using special long wooden rakes in a technique called "drawing the pans." Finally the salt crystals are dried in an oven, then packed, ready to use.

Milk chocolate Blended with salt and scattered with hazelnut nibs.

●●●Salt ●●Sweet ●●Milk ●●Hazelnut ●●Butter ●Cocoa 40%

Taste Light roast hazelnut; caramel; butter; cream. Hint of malt.

AMELIA ROPE
CHOCOLATE

PALE LIME & SEA SALT

Amelia Rope ✿

Zesty lime, vivid salt and relaxing indulgent waves of caramel: Amelia has created a heavenly fusion with these compelling flavours. **Amelia Rope says** The lime really brings the salt out to the fore and it is yummy! This is a new addition to the collection and catching up in popularity with the Pale Lemon & Sea Salt. **Cacao** Nacional from Ecuador. **Interestingly** This recipe idea came to Amelia as she watched people drinking tequila slammer cocktails and also recalling her favourite childhood sweet: those chewy bright green lime Opal Fruits which nowadays are called Starburst. Amelia also draws on her studies of aromatherapy when creating her handmade chocolates. Food grade organic aromatherapy oils are often selected.

Milk chocolate Blended with fine salt crystals and pale lime oil.

●●●Salt ●●Sweet ●●Milk ●●Butter ●●Cocoa 40% ●Lime

Taste Lime; salt; caramel; butter; cream. Hint of nut.

AMELIA ROPE WWW.AMELIAROPE.COM

PANAMA

Artisan du Chocolat

Charming hints of brown wood are delivered with finesse in waves of the silkiest, creamiest chocolate. Panama rewards those in search of substance and character in a medium milk chocolate. **Artisan du Chocolat say** An intense chocolate with notes of raisin and wood. **Cacao** Trinitario and criollo from the Talamanca mountain range on Panama's Caribbean coast. Fairly traded and organically grown. **Made** In Ashford, Kent, England. Bars are normally made from chocolate conched and refined in-house from cocoa liquor. **Established** Gerard founded Artisan du Chocolat in 2000 after training with Pierre Marcolini in Brussels. Since then, Gerard's chocolate creations have found their way onto the shelves of Fortnum & Mason, and onto the tables of Gordon Ramsay at Claridges and Heston Blumenthal's Fat Duck. For the former, he created an intense liquid salted caramel enclosed inside a cocoa dusted chocolate shell. For the latter, a tobacco dark chocolate.

Milk chocolate.

●●●Milk   ●●Cocoa 40%   ●●Sweet   ●●Butter

Taste Salt; brown sultana; smoky wood; hay; caramel; clotted cream; butter; brownie.

TONKA

Artisan du Chocolat ✿ ✿

A wonderful infusion that shows off the dried tonka bean's unique properties. The complex notes of this "distant cousin" of vanilla mingle with a creamy milk chocolate, then end sweetly with a little astringency. Characterised by distinctive but smooth and relaxing flavours that linger on the palate. **Artisan du Chocolat say** Tonka beans are the seeds of a large tree grown in the tropical regions of the Americas, particularly Mexico. Often used as a substitute for vanilla, these beans have a powerful smell of freshly cut hay, vanilla and bitter almonds. To capture their hypnotic fragrance, we crush the tonka beans and let them infuse for several days in a tank of molten milk chocolate. The result is a dynamic bar where the milk chocolate awakens and dances between comforting sweetness and powerful perfume. One of our all time favourites. **Interestingly** Tonka beans are banned in the United States by the Food and Drug Administration, who have conducted "tonka raids" on gourmet chef's kitchens. They are concerned that the bean contains coumarin, so, "may be especially risky for people taking blood-thinning drugs." Tonka beans are legal to use as an ingredient in just about every other country in the world. The beans are also widely used in perfumes for their special fragrance. The hardwood tonka tree, known as Brazilian teak, is native to the Amazon. Some examples have been dated as one thousand years old.

Milk chocolate Infused with tonka bean.

●●●Milk   ●●Sweet   ●●Tonka   ●●Cocoa 40%
●●Butter   ●●Vanilla

Taste Cherry; raw almond; marzipan; cream; vanilla gelato; maple syrup; hay; chocolate; cooking apple.

FUSION BAR

Cayoa St. Josef
Tampo or Espiritu Santo
Palm Sound
Gr. Coloosa
Mujacos
Hillsboro Inlet
Greenville Inlet
Bahama
Abaco

Boca Grand
Carlos I.
I. Macayo
Carlos B.
Blanco
Providence Chan.
Florida
Eleuthera I.
or Cigalco

Spanish Well
Punta Larga
Long Point
Cayo Sago
Cayo Largo
Andros

 I C

Richmond B.
Marquis I.
Providence
I.
Guanahana or Cat I. the first Land
of all America discovered by Columbus
in 1492 which he called St. Salvador.
Triangle

O

Tortuga Shoals
The Florida Stream
Kay Sal Bank
Santaren
Anguilla
Exuma or Soima
Exuma
Yuma or Long I.
Atwood Kay

BAHAMA BANK

St. Isabels
Rocks & Keys
ntonio
Havana
Matanzas
Ft. Pico
Matanzas
Oleybinger K.
Lobos K.
Old Chan. or Bahama
Crooked I.
Mogane or Aiguana I.
Crooked I.
Nth Caicus
Gt. Caicus
Turks Is.

Cortes
C. Gurral
St. Philips B. Porter B.
I. de Pinos
English K.
Jardin
Jardin del Reyna
Gulf of Xaxao
Puerto Principe
Chao
St. Jago or Cuba
C. Maize
Mouchoir Carre

Cape
Placer
Misteriosa
Lit. Caymanbrack
Caymanbrack
C. Cruz
Portilla
C. Cano
Cumberland Har.
Spinks
Gonayra
La Paz
Francais
ST. DOMINGO
Mole
St. Jago

BAY
Santanilla
rro or
angles
se
Swans I.
Grand
Cayman
Montego
St. Negril
JAMAICA
Trelaway
Spanish T.
Kingston
C. Doas Man
Grande
C. Tiburon
Morant
Los Cayes
Portau
Prince
or HISPANIOL
P. Domingo

OF
Cascable or
Rattle Snake
Savana la Mar
Pedro
Rocky
Bivora Bank
Port Royal
Grand Harbour
Morant Keys
Pto Grand
L. of Ax
Jaquemi
False
C. Mongon
Re Nieva
Saon P.

HONDURAS
Bonao
Honduras
C. Cameron
Brewers Lagoon
Hobbies K.
Sarenilla
Baxo Nuevo
or New Bone
Baxo del Comboy
or the Bugles

Coconut
Caratasco
Placer
English Banks or Pearl I.

unamakas
uizgalpa
Twacas
Woolvas
Sandy
Stany I.
Wawa Bluff
La Sacole
Seal K.
Pearl
CARIBBE

Roncadore
Mosnuitos
Catalina
Old Providence

L. Nicaragua
Mena
St. John
Green
Bluefields Bluff
Hene Sound
Corn K.
Celeridas
Turtles Mth
Porto Bello
THE
SPANISH MAIN
C. de Vela
Grande B.
Aruba

N.S. de los
Remedios
Ormo
S. Martha
Boncla
Maracaybo
Naero

Carthagena
Barbacoa
P. S. bernardo
Maracaybo
Lake

C. Blanco
G. of Salinas
cuencas
Dulce
Puerces B.
Porto Bello
St. Blas Pt.
Samba
G. of
Morosquillo
Carthagena
Magdalena
Zapatosa
Lake
Merida
Rocca del
Monte
MERIDA

C. Boral
los Remedios
Honda
M. of
Panama
BAY of
PANAMA
TERRAFIRMA
DARIEN
Caraquia
S O U T H

Hambuh
CHO CO
St. Fede
St. Juan
Apure
Guan
New

JAMAICA
Artisan du Chocolat ✤

A unique and distinctive chocolate that may surprise you with its gentle exotic flavours. The milk is luxurious; the texture is super-fine; the flavours are unusual. **Artisan du Chocolat say** Jamaican beans were the first cocoa beans imported to the United Kingdom in the late 16th century. Made into a milky drink, Jamaican cocoa was sold at first in apothecaries as a medicine. To revive this British innovation, we chose trinitario hybrid beans cultivated in small plantations around the parish of St Mary. These beans are fermented and dried at the Richmond Fermentary, roasted and ground, then conched and refined in our production in Kent. With a little cane sugar, the cocoa beans develop into a lovely rich dark chocolate bar with a melody of notes from liquorice to plums and jasmine. A must try. **Cacao** Trinitario from North East Jamaica. **Interestingly** On the fourth of May 1494, Christopher Columbus, on his second voyage, caught sight of "the fairest isle my eyes ever beheld." He named it Santiago. But its original indigenous name of Jamaica, or Xaymaca, persisted. Cacao was already being grown on the island by the Tainos, an Arawak speaking people, when the Spanish arrived. During the 1650s, the British captured Jamaica from the Spanish. It achieved independence from Britain in 1962. In 2011 Jamaica produced approximately 200 tonnes of cacao. **Pictured** 1799 map of the West Indies and Caribbean Sea.

Milk chocolate.

●●●Milk   ●●Sweet   ●●Cocoa 40%   ●Butter

Taste Jasmine; liquorice; smoke; caramel; lemongrass; gingerbread; coconut cream.

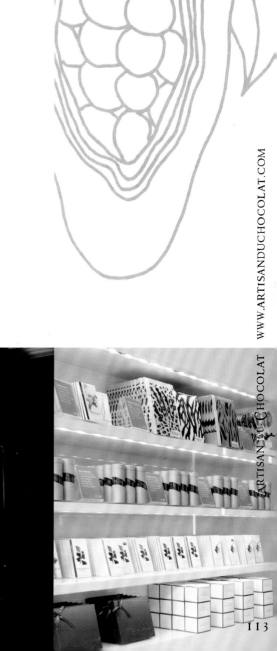

WWW.ARTISANDUCHOCOLAT.COM

ARTISAN DU CHOCOLAT

break the mould

Ginger & Lemongrass

GINGER & LEMONGRASS

Artisan du Chocolat ✪

The warming properties of ginger and cocoa in harmony with refreshing notes of lemongrass. The strength and pitch of the notes in this fusion are beautifully moderated: lively, but without sharpness. **Artisan du Chocolat say** According to traditional Chinese medicine, a healthy and happy life can only be achieved with the existence of a balance between Yin and Yang. Guided by the oldest instructions of Chinese food therapy, we created this bar by complimenting cocoa and ginger, both Yang foods that warm the body with cooling Yin lemongrass. A balanced and harmonious experience. **Interestingly** If travelling by British Airways First Class it is possible that you may be offered Artisan's gourmet chocolates during your flight. **Pictured** Left: lemongrass, native to Asia, can grow up to three or four feet. Above: ginger, which is grown for its juicy and sweet root, has not been found in the wild, so its origin is uncertain. But its use in southern Asia has been recorded as early as 400 BC.

Milk chocolate Blended with ginger and lemongrass.

●●●Sweet   ●●●Milk 26%   ●●Lemongrass   ●●Ginger   ●●Cocoa 40%   ●Butter

Taste Fresh ginger root; fresh lemongrass; milk chocolate brownie; cream. Hint of wood, tobacco, caramel, smoke and sultana.

Java

Artisan du Chocolat

Escape with delicate dreamy flavours that are almost whispered. Their subtlety encourages you to try one more piece, to consider the long-lasting smoky straw notes and the exceptionally smooth and creamy qualities. Gerard does not use vanilla, permitting all the details of this fine cocoa to be perceived. **Artisan du Chocolat say** The unusual notes of hay and smoke, from cacao beans grown on the rich volcanic soil of Java, are tamed by milk and sugar. Distinctive and exotic milk chocolate. **Cacao** Criollo and trinitario from Java, one of the largest islands of Indonesia. **Interestingly** In order to give Artisan du Chocolat's bars their super-fine texture, the chocolate has been pumped at high speed through a ball mill: a rotating cylinder filled with small loose stainless steel beads. Its action progressively reduces the bean's particle size from about three hundred microns to less than twenty microns: a size so fine that the human tongue is unable to detect it.

Milk chocolate.

●●●Milk ●●Sweet ●●Cocoa 40% ●Butter

Taste Double cream; straw; smoke; carob; café latte; butterscotch.

SAINT LUCIA MILK SEA SALT

Hotel Chocolat ⊗ ⊗

Rich sweet and savoury cocoa flavours, plus the sharpness from a pinch of salt make this chocolate deeply satisfying and especially tasty. **Hotel Chocolat say** All the deep cacao flavours of a great dark but with a dash of milk for a little mellowness. With hand harvested fleur de sel for balance and to cut through the sweetness. **Cacao** Trinitario from Saint Lucia, West Indies. **Established** Angus Thirlwell (whose father founded the iconic ice cream brand Mr. Whippy) co-founded Hotel Chocolat with fellow entrepreneur Peter Harris in 2003. Its first high street store opened in Watford, and now the company has more than thirty shops around the United Kingdom. In 2011 Hotel Chocolat opened their first shop in the United States, in Boston, Massachusetts. **Made** In Huntingdon, England.

Milk chocolate Blended with salt.

●●●Cocoa 50%   ●●Milk   ●●Salt   ●●Sweet
●Butter ●Sour ●Bitter

Taste Molasses; malt; charred wood; plum; smoke; cream; sea salt; dark chocolate mousse.

BRITISH
COCOA GROWER & CHOCOLATIER

SAINT LUCIA MILK CARAMEL

Hotel Chocolat ✣ ✣

Tangy dark milk chocolate, punctuated by crunchy caramel chips: a satisfying gastronomic treat. **Hotel Chocolat say** All the deep cacao flavours of a great dark but with a dash of milk for a little mellowness. To this base we have added tiny crushed caramel pieces that perfectly compliment the natural cream and caramel flavours of the chocolate, all overlaid with clean, fruity notes. **Cacao** Trinitario from Saint Lucia. **Interestingly** Hotel Chocolat has its own ethical trading and sustainability programme which partners with over one hundred and fifty growers in Saint Lucia. In addition to supplying seedlings at a subsidised rate, they guarantee to buy the planter's whole crop and pay them fairly and directly.

Milk chocolate Blended with vanilla. Containing caramel chips.

●●●Cocoa 50%   ●●Milk   ●●Sweet   ●●Butter   ●Caramel   ●Sour   ●Bitter

Taste Molasses; malt; charred wood; smoke; plum; cream; caramel; dark chocolate mousse.

SAINT LUCIA MILK
SEA SALT & CARAMEL

Hotel Chocolat ⊗ ⊗

A tangy, crunchy, and satisfying gastronomic treat. Dark yet creamy, punctuated with minute chewy caramel chippings and salt that fit right in with the lively cocoa. **Hotel Chocolat say** All the deep cacao flavours of a great dark, but with a dash of milk for a little mellowness. With crushed caramel pieces and hand harvested fleur de sel for balance and to cut through the sweetness. **Cacao** Trinitario from Saint Lucia. **Pictured** Hotel Chocolat do, in fact, have a hotel on their estate in Saint Lucia. On the 239 square mile Caribbean island with fertile volcanic soil, the plantation can be toured and guests may enjoy cocoa themed beauty treatments and cuisine.

Milk chocolate Blended with salt. Containing caramel chips.

●●●Cocoa 50%   ●●Milk   ●●Salt & Caramel   ●●Sweet
●●Butter ●Sour ●Bitter

Taste Molasses; malt; charred wood; smoke; plum; cream; sea salt; caramel; dark chocolate mousse.

Saint Lucia Milk Earl Grey Tea

Hotel Chocolat ✪ ✪ ✪

One of the greats. Dark, rustic, sweet and bitter around the edges, this chocolate accommodates the fruity and herbaceous tea flavours as if it was meant to be. **Hotel Chocolat say** Black tea scented with oil of bergamot that perfectly compliments the natural cream and caramel flavours of the chocolate. **Cacao** Trinitario, from one hundred and fifty growers on the island of Saint Lucia, including Hotel Chocolat's own Rabot Estate, where all the cacao is fermented. **Interestingly** Back in 1831, an employee of the British Prime Minister Charles Grey rescued the Chinese Mandarin's son from drowning. To show his gratitude, the Mandarin gave Earl Grey a unique blend of tea. Tea recipes were, and still are, highly valued by the Chinese. Earl Grey (left) liked the flavour so much that before he ran out of it he asked his tea merchant, Richard Twining, to recreate it. So Earl Grey was created especially for the Prime Minister to enjoy as his afternoon tea. It was first known as "Earl Grey's tea." **Pictured** Right: the cover of Hotel Chocolat's brochure celebrates the Queen's Diamond Jubilee in 2012, for which they released a special collection.

Milk chocolate Blended with minute tea leaves.

●●●Cocoa 50%　●●Milk　●●Tea　●●Sweet
●Butter　●Sour　●Bitter

Taste Wood; smoke; leather; lemon; lime; orange; tea leaf; milk.

125

RABOT ESTATE

C H.

FINE CACAO

Saint Lucia, West Indies

SAINT LUCIA MILK 50%
Hotel Chocolat ✿ ✿

It is the tangy, earthy flavours highlighted by lively sweet citrus and sesame seed that distinguish this superior dark milk chocolate. Deeply flavoursome, and satisfyingly robust. **Hotel Chocolat say** Opulent and seductive. Vibrant yellow fruit notes, then a caress of spiced cream. As little added sugar as a 70% dark chocolate - our high-cocoa milk chocolates satisfy with less. **Cacao** Trinitario from growers (including Hotel Chocoat's Rabot Estate, pictured) on the island of Saint Lucia, West Indies. **Interestingly** All of the seedlings on the Rabot Estate are created by grafting cuttings from the most prized cacao trees on the plantation. These trees have been identified by gene analysis at the University of Reading, back in England. Left: A cutting about 3cm long and 3mm deep, that has a bud, is taken from the branch of a desirable tree. It is placed into a cut of identical shape on the stem of a seedling, which is used only for its developed roots. Within days they become grafted together as if the tree was naturally healing a cut. All branches are removed except the one grown from the new bud. The resulting tree possesses only the genetic characteristics of the grafted cutting.

Milk chocolate Blended with vanilla.

●●●Cocoa 50% ●●Milk ●●Sweet ●Vanilla ●Sour ●Bitter

Taste Cream; sultana; wood; halva; berries; sweet lemon; dark caramel; molasses; wholemeal toast; tea.

Duffy's Star of Peru
Red Star Chocolate ✿ ✿

The distinctive taste of Peruvian cacao mellowed by rich milk, resulting in glorious fudgy nutty notes with a little fruit and spice also coming through. Vanilla is absent, enabling the subtleties of this intricate cocoa to be fully enjoyed. **Duffy says** Delicate flavours of blackcurrants and hazelnuts with warm spices in the aftertaste. **Cacao** Trinitario from Peru. **Made** In Cleethorpes in Lincolnshire. **Established** In 2009 by Duffy Sheardown, after being inspired by a radio program which said there were only two companies in Britain making chocolate directly from the beans. Duffy, a former Formula One engineer, crafts 30kg of chocolate per week starting with cacao beans, or liqueur. Each batch is granite-ground in a slow revolving conche for between forty and seventy hours, allowing the complex flavours to fully develop. Below: cacao shell tea.

Milk chocolate.

●●●Milk   ●●Sweet   ●●Butter   ●●Cocoa 40%   ●Sour   ●Bitter

Taste Double cream fudge; fresh grass; golden syrup; blackberry; toffee; hazelnut; elderflower; orange; ginger; cardamom; toast. Hint of fennel.

A warm, tender character. The multitude of harmonious tasteful flavours that emerge from the buttery melt can not be found anywhere else. **Duffy says** A lovely, creamy, milk chocolate that is hard to resist. Floral, with hints of hazelnuts, orange blossom and allspice. Made with organic sugar. **Cacao** Nacional from Guayas province, Ecuador. **Pictured** Although in general it can be said that the chocolate making process involves certain steps, the specific methods may vary considerably according to each cacaofèvier. Duffy makes chocolate in small batches using a mill called a melangeur to grind toasted, shelled, cocoa nibs until they become a thick paste. The grinding is continued until the paste becomes a smooth thick liquid. It takes about sixteen hours to reach this point. Then, as the wheels turn, finely ground sugar is added into the melangeur (left) and heat is applied from a pig lamp to maintain a temperature under 70°C. Intended to keep piglets warm, the lamp is one of Duffy's many innovations that enable small batch manufacture of chocolate. After a minimum of twenty four hours of grinding, milk powder is added. This final stage of grinding is called conching. It proceeds for a final thirty hours to ensure a smooth velvety texture by separating and coating all cocoa particles with cocoa butter. The heat generated also develops the flavours. Changes in flavour occur as acids, as well as water, evaporate from the chocolate. The time required for conching depends on the equipment used, the chocolate, and the flavour and texture objectives of the cacaofèvier. After conching the chocolate is tempered and moulded into bars.

Milk chocolate.

●●●Butter ●●Milk 18% ●Sweet ●Cocoa 43%

Taste Rose; elderflower; cream fudge; orange blossom; smoked nut; allspice; butterscotch. Hint of black pepper, roast hazelnut, roast peanut and sunflower oil.

DUFFY'S CORAZON DEL ECUADOR

Red Star Chocolate ✪

ORGANIC MILK
Rococo ✿

Classic deep and mid-range chocolaty notes with cream that progress to more intricate and intriguing flavours that fuel the imagination easily. **Rococo say** A lively cocoa-rich milk chocolate recipe with a dense encompassing texture, along with rich vanilla and caramel notes. **Cacao** A blend that includes trinitario beans from Rococo's own small organic cacao farm in north Grenada. Acquired in 2007 and named Grococo, its harvest is processed on the island by the Grenada Chocolate Company. **Pictured** A small portion from a batch of melted chocolate is spread out with a spatula on to a marble table to cool. Next, it is stirred back into the larger portion of chocolate to reduce its temperature. A little heat is applied to the chocolate again, then it is ready to mould into bars or novelties. This process, called tempering, enables the finished chocolate to have a nice glossy finish, even colour, and crisp texture. It also helps the chocolate to contract slightly as it cools for the final time, so that it releases easily from the mould. Tempering works by perfectly crystallising the cocoa butter in the chocolate into a stable form. It is pre-crystallised by the first decrease in temperature.

Milk chocolate Blended with vanilla.

●●●Sweet ●●Butter ●●Cocoa 37% ●Vanilla

Taste Bonfire toffee; molasses; sultana; roast; almond; tahini; allspice; cream; mint; honey; herbs. Hint of salt.

ROSE OTTO

Rococo ✿

The exotic and evocative gentle flavour of Turkish delight mingles with a sweet and creamy chocolate. Smooth, dreamy and delicious. **Rococo say** Rose scented organic milk chocolate. A luxury chocolate recipe which is intense, balanced, and long-lasting, with strong floral notes. **Cacao** An organic blend by Rococo that includes trinitario from their farm in Grenada. **Established** In Chelsea, London, 1983, by Chantal Coady. Prior to becoming a chocolatier, she had worked in the chocolate department of Harrods and had graduated in textile design. Her skills are evident in the charming and creative way that everything is presented at Rococo. Chantal is also the author of several books about chocolate. There are currently twenty five people employed at Rococo, which has three shops around the capital, and one in Chester. **Interestingly** The oil used by Rococo in this recipe is extracted gently from rose petals using steam distillation for a flavour that is delicate, but intensely floral and long-lasting. **Pictured** The second generation of Rococo packaging features designs inspired by the Moorish tiles in the garden behind the flagship shop in London's Belgravia. The original blue and white Rococo wrappers depict antique chocolate mould designs from a Létang Fils sales catalogue which Chantal bought at a Parisian flea market. Next to each design is its reference number, one of three pieces of information which are often stamped on antique moulds. The second being the trademark of the brand; and the third an identical one or two digit number used by the chocolatier to match the front and back of a mould, so that they may be clipped together. Létang became one of the world's first - and one of the most renowned - manufactures of metal chocolate moulds, after they were founded in 1832 in Paris. They were preceded only by Pinat (1820) and Cadot (1826) also in Paris. Létang moved to 108 Rue Vieille du Temple in 1891.

Milk chocolate Blended with vanilla and rose essential oil.

●●●Sweet   ●●Rose Oil   ●●Milk   ●Butter   ●Cocoa 37%

Taste Rose; Turkish delight; chocolate mousse; chocolate cake. Hint of lychee.

EL BLANCO
Willie's Cacao ✽

El Blanco has a fine texture as it melts sweetly in the mouth. It has the lush taste of fresh whole milk, with complex sweet and savoury details to discover. **Willie says** This is white chocolate as it should be, light and milky. The secret is beautiful ingredients and balance. Natural Venezuelan cacao butter, sugar cane from Guadeloupe and British milk, all in perfect harmony. **Cacao** Trinitario from Venezuela. **Made** In Uffculme, Devon. **Established** In 2007 (as El Tesoro) by Willie Harcourt-Cooze (pictured). When exploring Venezuela in 1993, it was on the advice of a beach umbrella salesman that Willie stumbled on a thousand acre cacao farm, Hacienda el Tesoro, in the Henri Pittier National Park (left). Three years later he and his wife sold everything they had in order to buy it. And so started a maverick project to make pure chocolate back in Devon and to educate the British consumer about the delights of it. This was documented in the television series Willy's Wonky Chocolate Factory and Willie's Chocolate Revolution. Willie inspired viewers to use his first product, a 100% cylinder of cacao (lower left) that could be used as a cooking ingredient, with demonstrations of how versatile chocolate is in sweet and savoury recipes. Over the years Willie has written two books (Willie's Chocolate Bible and Chocolate Factory Cookbook) and developed his product range to include cylinders, bars and chilled desserts using single origin cacao from around the world. As well as experiencing growing international demand and distribution, Willie's succeeded in being selected by prestigious national retailers Waitrose, Selfridges and Harvey Nichols.

Non-deodorised white chocolate.

●●●Milk ●●●Sweet ●Butter

Taste Heather honey; lavender; golden syrup; Brazil nut; cashew nut; coconut; fudge; malted milk; sweet corn.

WILLIES CACAO CACAOFEVIER WWW.WILLIESCACAO.COM

137

FRANCE

NATURE
Bernachon ⊗ ⊗

"Nature" has warm, earthy tones thanks to a sensational blend of cocoas, intricately flavoured hazelnut, graceful caramelised notes and a complete and creamy milk. A pinch of salt heightens the contrast and complexity. **Bernachon say** Our chocolates possess an outstanding flavour. The raw cacao beans, selected for their prestigious quality, are processed on site. They are roasted, ground, blended and conched in-house. **Cacao** A blend of several origins. **Established** In 1953. Maurice Bernachon entered the world of chocolate at the age of fourteen as apprentice to Mr Debauge in Pont de Beauvoisin and later Mr Coillard in rue Victor Hugo, Lyon. Later he joined the workshop of master chocolatier Durand on Cours Franklin. Upon his retirement in 1953, Durand gave Bernachon the opportunity to take over his chocolate and confectionary shop. Maurice Bernachon worked on with his son Jean-Jacques and fifty employees. When Maurice retired, Jean-Jacques, who was married to the daughter of the great chef Paul Bocuse, took over the family business. Today their children Candice, Stéphanie and Philippe Bernachon (pictured with their mother) continue the tradition at the same premises. **Made** In the workshop behind Bernachon's shop, restaurant and salon de thé on Cours Franklin Roosevelt, Lyon.

Milk chocolate Blended with vanilla, hazelnut paste and a trace of salt.

●●Sweet ●●Milk ●●Butter ●●Cocoa 20% Solids ●●Vanilla ●Hazelnut ●Salt

Taste Roast; caramel; fresh hazelnut; full cream milk; peanut; sultana; banana; butter; salt. Hint of almond.

Bernachon Cacaofévrier www.bernachon.com

NOISETTES
Bernachon ✿ ✿

The pale hazelnuts have been placed by hand in a particular order, to ensure that there is one in every square that you break off. Their taste is unique: complex, lively and fresh. When munched, their taste converges with that of the tender nutty chocolate creating an experience on a par with the finest desserts. **Bernachon say** Milk chocolate filled with grilled Piedmont hazelnuts. Special care is given to the making of chocolate bars, which are the foundation of the master chocolatier. **Cacao** A blend of several origins. **Interestingly** Philippe Bernachon creates his chocolate with the original recipes and Dutch machines that were passed down to him by his father, and his grandfather before him. Each 150g tablette (bar) is wrapped by hand. A unique feature of the Bernachon label is that the percentage of cocoa solids in the chocolate is stated, rather than the common method of including cocoa butter in the figure. This provides a better indication of how dark the chocolate might taste. **Pictured** To give the chocolate hen its colourful details, a mould was prepared by painting it with white chocolate combined with food colouring before the chocolate was poured in. Cocoa butter was also used at the same stage in order to give the chocolate's surface a high gloss finish. Some of it was mixed with gold leaf.

Milk chocolate Blended with hazelnut paste. With whole hazelnuts laid on one side.

●●Hazelnut   ●●Butter   ●●Milk   ●●Sweet
●●Cocoa 20% Solids

Taste Fresh hazelnut; whole milk; cream; roast hazelnut; chocolate cake; molasses. Hint of salt, peanut and yeast.

BERNACHON CACAOFÉVIER WWW.BERNACHON.COM

JOUR ET NUIT

Bernachon ✪ ✪

The dramatic juxtaposition of equal proportions of dark and milk hazelnut chocolate sets the stage for a complete fusion of complimentary flavours. The nut notes embedded in the long-lasting cocoa are extraordinary and it's full of references to dark semi-sweet flavours such as dried fruit. **Cacao** A blend of several origins. **Pictured** The Palet d'Or (Gold Medal) the house speciality of fresh cream and dark chocolate, is hand dipped and allowed to cool on flakes of edible (22-24 carat) gold leaf. It is beaten to one tenth of a micron thin in the Excenevex workshop of Georges Dauvet (above left) "batteur d'or" for three generations.

Dark and milk chocolate Moulded together in two layers. Both blended with hazelnut paste and vanilla.

●●●Cocoa 55%   ●●Hazelnut   ●●Sweet   ●Milk   ●Vanilla   ●Bitter

Taste Cream; fresh hazelnut; roast hazelnut; almond; butter; coffee; molasses; dark chocolate cake; fig; cinnamon; apricot; yeast.

An exquisite marriage: the most tender, gentle and tangy slices of crystallised orange lay in Bernachon's great hazelnut milk chocolate. An impeccable composition of flavours. **Bernachon say** Magnifying flavour, the tradition-bearing Bernachon house has made chocolate crafting a mastered art. Thanks to rigorously selected raw cacao beans and perfect roasting, the Bernachon family creates ephemeral works of art whose proportions and balance are equalled only by the taste sensations they offer. **Cacao** A blend of several origins. **Interestingly** In their book with Rose Beranbaum, *A Passion for Chocolate,* Maurice and Jean-Jacques Bernachon describe their ten day recipe for candied orange peel. A small amount of pith is left on the slices of peel to add a pleasant sourness. They are boiled for several minutes before being drained, plunged into ice water and drained again to set their vibrant colour and halt the cooking process. Next, water, sugar and vanilla are brought to the boil whilst being constantly stirred. The pan is removed from the heat and the orange peels are added without stirring. The pan is then covered and set aside at room temperature for several hours. The next step then takes place and it is repeated on each of the following nine days: the mixture is uncovered and heated for about five minutes, then covered and set aside once again. The final step is to drain the orange peels and cut them into lengths before allowing them to dry for several hours.

Milk chocolate Blended with hazelnut paste. Containing slices of candied orange peel.

●●Orange   ●●Hazelnut   ●●Butter   ●●Milk   ●●Cocoa 20%   ●●Sweet   ●Vanilla

Taste Hazelnut; almond; lightly candied orange; whole milk; cream; malt; light roast; caramel.

ORANGE
Bernachon ✳ ✳ ✳

IVOIRE

Bernachon ✿ ✿

We must begin with the almonds that characterise this unique white chocolate: who knows where they are from or how they are prepared? And you will wonder, because they contribute such a detailed and expressive range of flavours. Ivoire is an elegant and amiable chocolate: it pleases with rounded almond, butter, vanilla and cream tones. **Bernachon say** To give chocolate a shape and a name is the aspiration of the Bernachon family. "Chocolate is not a treat or a sweet but true gourmet food." -Maurice Bernachon. **Interestingly** Nuts are refined by metal rollers (right and below) producing soft flakes that may be blended into chocolate, used to make macaroons or ganache. Bernachon's President cake is decorated with chocolate flakes produced the same way (background below).

White chocolate Blended with vanilla and almond paste.

●●●Butter   ●●●Sweet   ●●Almond   ●●Vanilla
●●Milk

Taste Almond; double cream; vanilla; salt; meringue; flour. Hint of caramel, peanut and cashew.

BERNAC.
42, COURS FRANKLIN
69006 LYON - FR
TEL. 04 78 24 37

CAFÉ AU LAIT

Bernachon ⊗ ⊗

Bernachon's suave hazelnut milk chocolate with a filling: finely roasted Colombian coffee beans have been ground with hazelnuts and cocoa into a luxurious flaky paste. It has an ever-so-slight texture to it that melts softly, bringing the trio of flavours together beautifully. **Cacao** A blend of several origins. **Interestingly** Below right: the cake that Bernachon named "Le President" in 1975. It was presented at the fiftieth birthday of President Valéry Giscard d'Estaing. It was originally called "Le Montmorency" because it features Montmorency sour cherries. It is finished with tender chocolate flakes that are refined between large rollers. The chef has a little secret to avoid the flakes melting in his hands as he decorates the cake: it is to (carefully) touch the stone roller to cool them down.

Milk chocolate Blended with hazelnut paste and vanilla. Filled with a hazelnut and coffee praline.

●●●Sweet   ●●Butter   ●●Coffee   ●●Hazelnut
●●Cocoa   ●●Milk   ●Vanilla

Taste Cream; whole milk; medium roast coffee; roast hazelnut; caramel; malt.

Bernachon Cacaofévier www.bernachon.com

BIOLOGIQUE

Organic Milk Chocolate
Bonnat ✿ ✿

This is a creamy and silky chocolate with an emphasis on profound savoury cocoa notes. These lingering flavours might make you think of nuts and yeast in particular. As with all of Bonnat's chocolates, there is a rare purity to the taste, because it is free from vanilla, as well as the cloying buttery aspect often found in suave chocolates. **Cacao** Organic from a single origin. **Established** The art of chocolate making has been passed from father to son at Bonnat in Voiron since 1884. Bonnat are the oldest family-run cacaofévier in France. **Interestingly** Bonnat's maxim is printed on the back of each bar, "What's good for the palate does no harm to the soul."

Milk chocolate.

●●●Milk ●●Cocoa 55% ●Butter ●Sweet ●Bitter

Taste Hay; yeast; tahini; walnut; mascarpone; cream; toffee; mocha; chocolate. Hint of smoke, honey, cherry and vanilla halva.

153

JAVA

Bonnat ✻ ✻ ✻

Java has a high content of fine cocoa which is presented gracefully on waves of the finest cream. This reveals delicate, yet profound, lingering flavours. Java's sweetness and bitterness are gentle and refined, completing the sumptuous experience. If Rolls Royce made chocolate, it might taste like this. Stéphane Bonnat uses sugar with great restraint and vanilla is prohibited. This gives a very clean and fresh flavour to his chocolate and allows the taste buds to perceive every detail of the milk and prestigious cocoa. **Cacao** From Java, Indonesia. **Pictured** Above: the chocolatier next to the winnower, which separates the roasted cacao beans from their husks. Right: the Sirocco ball roaster.

Milk chocolate.

●●●Milk   ●●●Cocoa 65%   ●Sweet   ●Butter ●Bitter

Taste Double cream; a drop of honey; molasses; malt; hay; smoke; coffee. Hint of lemon zest.

Bonnat · Cacaofévier · www.bonnat-chocolatier.com

SURABAYA

Bonnat ⊗ ⊗ ⊗

Bonnat do not make milk chocolate, they make cream chocolate. Surabaya presents sophisticated bitter, sour and savoury flavours very gently, in the freshest, finest cream imaginable. **Cacao** From Surabaya, on the island of Java, Indonesia. **Interestingly** The name of Indonesia's second largest city is derived from a great white shark (sura) and a giant crocodile (baya) who are said to have fought each other to prove their strength. They are depicted on the city's coat of arms.

Milk chocolate.

●●●Milk ●●●Cocoa 65% ●●Butter ●Sweet ●Bitter ●Sour

Taste Double cream; halva; carob; grapefruit pith; smoke; yeast. molasses; walnut oil; black olive. Hint of coffee, Marmite, liquorice and beef stock.

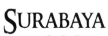

Bonnat Cacaofévier www.bonnat-chocolatier.com

SANS SUCRE AJOUTÉ

Bonnat ✪

Bonnat's "No Added Sugar" possesses three notable qualities: impeccably refined, yet earthy, cocoa; luxuriously smooth thick cream; and the conservative use of maltitol to create an agreeable sweetness that promotes the first two qualities. The cocoa is particularly suited to the use of maltitol, taming the sweetener in just the right areas, creating a most interesting dark cream chocolate with formidable flavours.

Interestingly Bonnat's chocolate wrapper artwork, which has not changed in one hundred years, shows the view of the church of Saint Bruno in the town centre, as seen from the chocolatier's window. The impressive spires are based on drawings by architect Viollet-le-Duc, who added the spire to the famous church of Notre-Dame during his restoration of it.

Milk chocolate Sweetened with maltitol. No added sugar.

●●●Milk   ●●●Cocoa 55%
●●Butter ●Sweet ●Bitter

Taste Double cream; buffalo mozzarella; smoke; earth; tobacco; yeast; sesame; grapefruit pith. Hint of coffee, caramel, Marmite and beef stock.

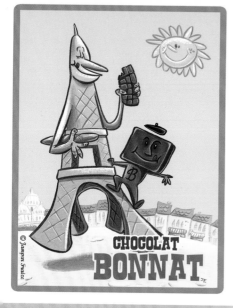

CHOCOLAT BONNAT

CHOCOLAT BONNAT

© Jampur Fraize

CHOCOLAT BONNAT

© Jampur Fraize

CHOCOLAT BONNAT

© Jampur Fraize

CHOCOLAT BONNAT

© Jampur Fraize

CHOCOLAT BONNAT

© Jampur Fraize

IVOIRE
Bonnat ✿ ✿

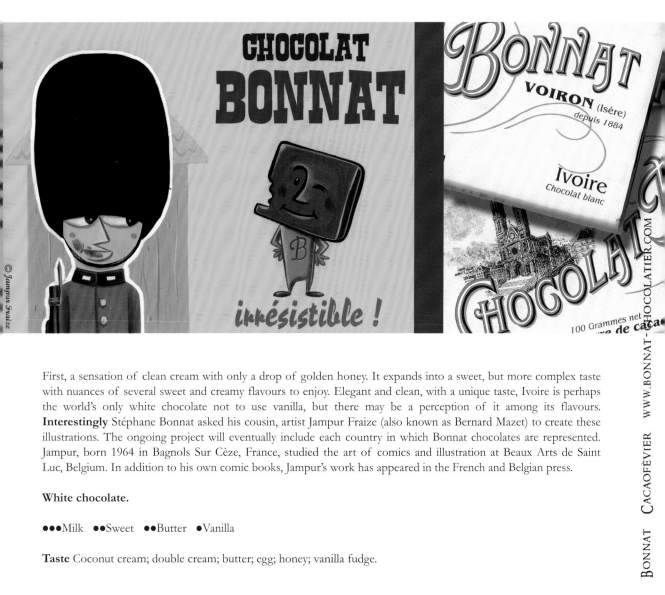

First, a sensation of clean cream with only a drop of golden honey. It expands into a sweet, but more complex taste with nuances of several sweet and creamy flavours to enjoy. Elegant and clean, with a unique taste, Ivoire is perhaps the world's only white chocolate not to use vanilla, but there may be a perception of it among its flavours. **Interestingly** Stéphane Bonnat asked his cousin, artist Jampur Fraize (also known as Bernard Mazet) to create these illustrations. The ongoing project will eventually include each country in which Bonnat chocolates are represented. Jampur, born 1964 in Bagnols Sur Cèze, France, studied the art of comics and illustration at Beaux Arts de Saint Luc, Belgium. In addition to his own comic books, Jampur's work has appeared in the French and Belgian press.

White chocolate.

●●●Milk ●●Sweet ●●Butter ●Vanilla

Taste Coconut cream; double cream; butter; egg; honey; vanilla fudge.

CHOCOLAT AU LAIT
Bonnat ✿ ✿

A refreshing, crisp cream gradually and elegantly reveals the cocoa's depth. As it melts away, you experience a curious evolution of smoky and roasted cacao flavours that are free from bitterness and acidity. **Interestingly** The coat of arms of the Rhône-Alpes, in which Bonnat is situated, features a dolphin because it incorporates an ancient region known as Dauphiné. This is the reason why two ancient dolphins surround Bonnat's own coat of arms. A 70cm high chocolate replica may be seen on the "Surabaya" page.

Milk chocolate.

●●●Milk ●●Cocoa 55% ●●Sweet
●●Butter ●Bitter

Taste Fresh cream; hay; smoked wood chips; molasses; malt; honey; cherry; flower. Hint of spice and clove.

ASFARTH

Bonnat ⊗ ⊗ ⊗

Asfarth presents earthy flavours in a highly refined manner. Like the other chocolates in Bonnat's Asiatic trilogy (Java and Surabaya) they have been balanced with rich, but silky, cream. The taste is especially pure: without the oily taste from cocoa butter often found in extra-smooth chocolates; without any vanilla; and with unobtrusive use of sugar. This smoky chocolate has characteristics of unsweetened coffee, tobacco and muted citrus peel. The hint of dry cocoa flourishes in the aftertaste. **Cacao** From Sumatra, Indonesia. **Interestingly** Every Bonnat chocolate bar is inscribed with "Pour croquer," which means for munching, or eating. In the old days it distinguished the bars from the majority which were used for making drinking chocolate.

Milk chocolate.

●●●Milk   ●●●Cocoa 65%   ●●Butter   ●Sweet   ●Sour   ●Bitter

Taste Double cream; grapefruit zest; butter; earth; smoke; tobacco. Hint of cappuccino, caramel and candied grapefruit.

CRÈME DE PRALINÉ

Chapon

It is the breadth of tasteful flavours and textures that makes this crunchy paste so engaging. Smooth, tender flavours come from a superb selection of nuts, light and dark cocoa notes, and a drop of milk. The minute caramel brittle pieces give Crème de Praliné a moderate sweetness which, like the wood smoked salt, permits the many flavours to play on the tongue.

Chapon say Simply divine. Serve at room temperature at breakfast or dinner, it will also be your treat for dessert, warmed slightly and accompanied by vanilla ice cream.

Made in Chelles, east of Paris.

Established It was whilst appointed as ice cream and sorbet maker to Her Majesty The Queen at Buckingham Palace, that Patrice Chapon first became fascinated by the idea of creating fine chocolate, after being inspired by the window displays at Harrods. During this time he found his mascot, "the three boys" on a chocolate box, in a London antique shop. Back in France in 1985, Patrice created his first chocolates in the cellar of the family home. He made them each morning and sold them to shops in the afternoon. The doors to his first shop opened in 2001 in Paris.

Milk chocolate paste Blended with smoked salt, hazelnut, almond, and pistachio pastes. Containing minute pieces of caramel brittle.

●●Salt ●Cocoa ●Butter ●Milk
●Sweet ●Nut

Taste Caramel and nut brittle; crème brûlée; brandy snap; clay; salt; roast almond; roast hazelnut; roast pistachio; milk chocolate; dark chocolate; sesame.

ÉCLATS CARAMEL BEURRE SALÉ

Michel Cluizel ✤

A duet between plentiful brittle caramel chips, which melt in the mouth, and smooth, dark milk chocolate. Its very chocolaty character, and the sensual aspects of the caramel, are encouraged by a touch of Guérande salt. **Cluizel say** The delicately salted, enthusiastically crunchy, fine butter caramel delights the palate, with a final twist of creamy chocolate. **Made** In Damville, Normandy. Situated 115km West of Paris, France. **Established** In 1948 by Michel Cluizel and his parents Marc and Marcelle Cluizel, who were pastry chefs. The chocolatier now has boutiques in Paris and New York. Cluizel's workshops in Normandy employ over two hundred people and include a shop and a five hundred square metre chocolate museum called the Chocolatrium. **Pictured** Right: les Champignons, mushrooms made with caramel, nougat and chocolate. Definitely an edible variety.

Milk chocolate Blended with vanilla. Containing chips of salted butter caramel.

●●●Butter   ●●Cocoa 45%   ●●Milk   ●●Sweet   ●●Vanilla
●●Caramel   ●Salt

Taste Salted butter; dark caramel; chocolate; whole milk. Hint of roast, carob, tobacco, hazelnut.

GRAND LAIT AUX NOISETTES

Michel Cluizel ✣

They seem to have been made for each other: the hazelnut's gentle characteristics mingle with and enhance the smooth tones of this classic chocolate. Just the right proportions have been used. **Cluizel say** The hazelnuts are slowly roasted and delicately ground, allowing their unique and subtle aroma to infuse the chunky, crunchy chocolate. Created in Michel Cluizel's chocolaterie, with a blend of cocoa beans from several origins, these fine milk chocolates stand out from others by their cocoa content and specific added ingredients. **Pictured** Above: hazelnuts before harvest. **Interestingly** Hazelnuts can now be found across the world, from Scotland to Australia. Turkey is the world's biggest producer of the nut, exporting around one hundred thousand tonnes per year.

Milk chocolate Blended with vanilla. Containing large hazelnut nibs.

●●Milk ●Sweet ●●Butter ●●Cocoa 45% ●Hazelnut ●Vanilla

Taste Honey; chocolate; cream; light roast hazelnut; butterscotch. Hint of salt, molasses and roast.

Michel Cluizel   Cacaofévier   www.cluizel.com

171

COUPELLE FLORALIE

12.00 €

Prix au kg : 181.82 €

66 g

MICHEL CLUIZEL

B.N72

MICHEL CLUIZEL

GRAND LAIT

Michel Cluizel ✿

A great creamy chocolaty flavour with influences of butterscotch and honey. Simple and satisfying, melting with an exceedingly fine texture. **Cluizel say** Very crunchy Grand Lait that melts in the mouth with hints of brown caramel, liberates intense and condensed milky notes and eventually comes back to tonalities of very sweet milk caramel. **Cacao** A blend of several origins. **Interestingly** The family-run chocolatier create all of their chocolate from the beans, which they purchase directly from the plantations, paying two to three times the general market value. **Pictured** Michel Cluizel. Far left: milk chocolate baguettes and a jar containing cocoa beans in Cluizel's shop, Paris.

Milk chocolate Blended with vanilla.

●●●Butter ●●Milk ●●Sweet ●●Cocoa 45% ●Vanilla

Taste Honey; chocolate; cream; ripe banana; butterscotch. Hint of salt, bread, molasses and roast.

MICHEL CLUIZEL CACAOFÉVIER WWW.CLUIZEL.COM

IVOIRE
Michel Cluizel ✿ ✿

Imagine an indulgent vanilla milkshake. One created with the finest ingredients from the pantry of an elite gourmet restaurant. **Michel Cluizel says** With its sweet hints of milk and vanilla, the ivory chocolate bar falls within the tradition of white chocolate classics and will satisfy great white chocolate lovers with its complete sweetness. **Interestingly** The world's first white chocolate bar was probably Galak, by Nestlé. It was first produced in the 1930's in Switzerland and it continues to be sold today in some countries.

White chocolate Blended with vanilla.

●●●Vanilla   ●●Sweet   ●●Milk   ●●Butter

Taste Thick vanilla milkshake; meringue; vanilla ice cream. Hint of ripe banana.

Smooth chocolate with suave creamy notes, fortified by lasting flavours of Christmas pudding. **Cluizel say** With an exceptional cocoa content, the world's first "1er Cru de Plantation" [single plantation] milk chocolate is composed only of very characteristic, light-coloured beans produced by the Mangaro plantation in the North-West of the island of Madagascar. It expresses, in a highly refined blend, notes of caramel, exotic fruits, warm spice cake and honey, completed, in the finale, with sultanas. **Cacao** From the Sambirano river valley, Madagascar. **Interestingly** The plantation's name is due to the fact that it was formerly a forest of mango trees. Right: Michel Cluizel and son Marc.

Milk chocolate Blended with vanilla.

●●●Cocoa 50%   ●●Milk   ●●Vanilla   ●Sweet   ●Butter   ●Sour

Taste Tobacco; smoke; molasses; cream; clear honey; dark chocolate brownie; malt; Christmas pudding; raw almond. Hint of unsweetened ginger and salt.

MANGARO
Michel Cluizel ✳ ✳

Michel Cluizel · Cacaofèvier · www.cluizel.com

177

MARALUMI

Michel Cluizel ✧ ✧ ✧

Intense and engaging from the first moment. Fantastic toffee, treacle and herb flavours are nicely rounded off with smooth, creamy, cappuccino. The hints of fruit make it extra special. **Cluizel say** This strongly aromatic milk chocolate expresses in the mouth the characteristic notes of bananas, red berries and blueberries. They emanate progressively in a herbaceous harmony and then in salty caramel. **Cacao** Trinitario from a single plantation near the East coast of Papua New Guinea. **Interestingly** Mr Cluizel, who has been producing chocolate from the beans for over sixty five years, observes, "These days, machines have enabled us to improve the quality of our chocolate immensely. As long as we possess our know-how from the past, the situation is that thanks to our ingenious staff we can modify the machines available on the market to satisfy our demand for quality... and not the reverse."

Milk chocolate Blended with vanilla.

●●●Cocoa 47%   ●●●Milk   ●●Sweet   ●●Butter   ●Vanilla   ●Sour

Taste Treacle; caramel; coffee; cream; herbs; gingerbread; liquorice; ripe banana; malt; blueberry; lemon; salt.

CÔTE D'IVOIRE LACTÉ

Le Chocolat Alain Ducasse ✿

An impressively rich and tangy chocolate distinguished by five flavour elements: salt, caramel, butter, full milk and gutsy cocoa. Each element is complimentary to the others and equally strong, creating unison. There is a very slight texture to play on the tongue. **Cacao** Forastero from Ivory Coast, West Africa. **Established** February 18th 2013 by Alain Ducasse, who holds the honour of being the first chef ever to earn three Michelin stars for three different restaurants (Paris, Monaco and New York). Ducasse acts as the artistic director, defining flavours with Nicolas Berger, who is entrusted with directing the workshop. In the 1970s Ducasse was an apprentice to Michel Guérard, and he learned about pastry from Gaston Lenôtre. Ducasse went to Paris to meet Michel Chaudun, where he discovered that pastry excited him more than he could ever know. From there, Ducasse began working for Alain Chapel in Mionnay. He devoted his days off to work beside Maurice Bernachon in Lyon. Berger, who met Ducasse in 2000, was introduced to the art of the chocolatier as a child. He spent days with his father, coating bonbons in his workshop. He went on to work at Hévin, Peltier and Ladurée in Paris. Later he became corporate pastry chef for the entire Ducasse group of establishments, overseeing the kitchens around the globe. **Made** In Bastille, Paris. The shop and factory are situated at the back of a cobbled courtyard on the former site of a Renault garage. Visitors can watch the production of chocolates through a glass partition in the shop. **Interestingly** Nicolas Berger travelled all over Europe to source equipment, inspecting many old machines before purchasing a Virey Garnier coffee roaster. He adapted it to roast cacao by lowering its working temperature to 70°C. The speed at which its cylinder rotates was also reduced, so as not to break the cacao beans, which are more delicate. A more uniform roast is possible by avoiding mixing whole and broken beans. Other machines include a Bühler roll mill and a Pedzholdt conche.

Milk chocolate Blended with vanilla and salt.

●●Cocoa 35%   ●●Milk   ●●Sweet   ●●Butter   ●●Salt

Taste Brownie; chocolate fudge; salted caramel; cream; malt; sultana; caramelised hazelnut; molasses; shortbread. Hint of golden syrup and condensed milk.

AMANDES, FIGUES, ORANGES, CONFITES...

Le Chocolat Alain Ducasse ⊛

This complex cocoa-rich chocolate fuses superbly with every one of the first class dried fruits and nuts that cover it. Each tangy bite varies in its flavour, but the theme, balance and quality are consistent. The fruits are tender. The nuts have a crisp lightly sugared exterior and are delicate inside. They balance the sweet, bitter, sour, salty, milky, vanillary chocolate in just the right places to create a sensational harmony. **Alain Ducasse says** Chocolate is a promise of bliss, to which we voluptuously relinquish ourselves. It bewitches me to an ineffable point. It opens doors to imagination and creation. This noble and demanding ingredient is the fruit of a precise craft, one who's hidden riches can only be revealed by the artisan chocolatier. Like a hidden treasure, it demands a high level of method, precision and proficiency. I invite you into this unique world. **Pictured** Right: in addition to numerous cookery books, Ducasse has produced culinary guides to Paris, New York and Monaco. Far right: the factory. Its heavy steel gates with brass handles once guarded a Bank of France. The suspended lamps once hung from a 1930's military ship.

Milk chocolate Blended with vanilla and salt. Scattered on one side with caramelised pine nuts, almonds, hazelnuts, pistachios, orange, figs and currants.

●●●Cocoa 45% ●●Sweet ●●Milk ●●Butter ●Bitter ●Salt ●Vanilla ●Sour ●Fruits ●Nuts

Taste Light roast hazelnut, pine nut; pistachio and almond; honey; cream; white toast; dark chocolate fudge; brownie; molasses; salted caramel; red wine; blueberry; raspberry.

NICARAGUA 65%

Friis-Holm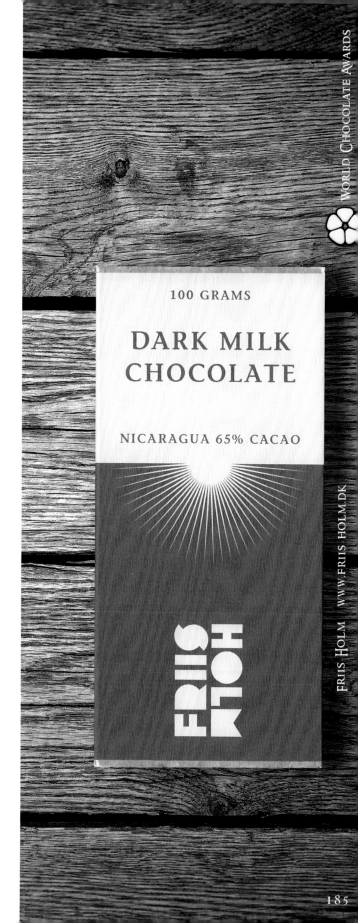

Nicaragua has a tremendously indulgent creamy character. Imagine the clean taste of rich cream that you can stand a spoon in. It is underscored after a few moments by a feast of innumerable subtle flavours that constantly evolve as the silky chocolate melts away. These complex medium and deep roasted cacao notes are engaging and detailed despite the extravagant proportion of milk. The aftertaste is of deep roasted cacao with hints of charred wood. **Friis-Holm say** A creamy start followed by a cinnamon-spicy dark berry caramel. Ending in a powerful chocolaty finish and a refreshing bitterness in the back of the mouth. **Cacao** A blend of six varieties of trinitario and criollo sourced from the Xoco Fine Cocoa Company: Chuno, Nicaliso, Rugoso, Johe, Medalla and Barba. All are cultivated in Nicaragua, the country where they were discovered. **Made** Exclusively for Friis-Holm by Bonnat in Voiron, France. **Established** In 2000 by Mikkel Friis-Holm as an importer and distributor of Scharffen Berger chocolate. This small family business, based in Denmark, specialises in imported fine foods such as olive oils, preserves and teas. In 2010 Friis-Holm launched its own range of five dark and two milk chocolates after participating in a project with Oxco Fine Cocoa Company to find and evaluate rare types of cacao in Nicaragua and Honduras. "Literally thousands of different cacao were tasted and tested on the way to the final selection," Mikkel explained. The selected types of cacao were then propagated by Xoco in probably the largest grafting program the world had ever seen. **Interestingly** Robert Steinberg (1947-2008) co-founder of Scharffen Berger chocolate was the first investor in Xoco.

Milk chocolate.

●●●Milk   ●●Butter   ●●Cocoa 65%   ●●Bitter ●●Sweet

Taste Clotted cream; milk chocolate mousse. Hint of cinnamon; caramel; blackberry; pale sultana; fig; fresh ginger root, unsweetened liquorice; almond; tobacco; charred wood.

FRIIS HOLM   WWW.FRIIS-HOLM.DK

Vietnam

Chocolaterie A.Morin ✤ ✤

The evolution starts with a creamy, chocolaty, introduction, from which vivacious fruity notes emerge. Morin explores the delicious sweet and acidic aspects of this cacao in a very tasteful way: never acute, yet far from muted. It feels adventurous and lively. Perhaps kiwi and sweet white grape best describe these notes. They are constantly backed by tangy fig and mellow malted chocolate milkshake flavours. **Cacao** Trinitario from the Mekong Delta, south-western Vietnam. **Interestingly** Cacao was first introduced to Vietnam by the French in 1878 along with several other cash crops. Cacao farming never took off, despite a subsidy. "It seems effectively useless to encourage this culture which has, until now, not yielded any satisfying result," the governor wrote in 1907. Several other initiatives over the decades have also failed. Only a few trees remained. However in recent years higher cacao prices, international initiatives and easier access to the world market have helped to significantly change the situation. Production is now over 5000 tons per year, and climbing. **Established** In 1958 by André Morin in Donzère. However to appreciate the family's heritage as chocolatiers we must look further back in time: 1868 was the year that the monks of the abbey Aiguebelle founded the Chocolaterie d'Aiguebelle, and in 1884 Gustave Morin began working as chocolatier and confectioner there. André followed in his father's footsteps, becoming responsible for the production of sweets and chocolate until growth of the company brought with it changes to the methods of work. This was why in 1958 he built his own chocolate factory to make products of the highest quality. **Made** In Donzère, Drôme, Provence. The workshop, with shop, is situated 160km south of Lyon and 14km South of Montélimar.

Milk chocolate.

●●●Sweet   ●●Milk   ●●Cocoa 40%   ●●Butter   ●●Sour

Taste Molasses; chocolate; tobacco; dried fig; sultana; caramel; malt; kiwi; cherry; white grape. Hint of orange peel and smoke.

LAIT BOLVIE SAUVAGE 40%

Chocolaterie A. Morin ✼

A satisfyingly tangy, creamy, fudgy chocolate, with good complexity. After a few moments special notes of seed, cereal and mild fruit develop. Morin's chocolates always possess a smooth and extraordinarily flavoursome sweetness: never sharp or saturating. You will be left with pleasing aftertaste of chocolate and cream. **Cacao** Harvested from wild trees in Bolivia. **Pictured** The Morin workshop is unique: located in one of the sunniest regions of France, it is surrounded by apple, pear, apricot, cherry and almond orchards that André Morin planted in order to provide the best fresh raw materials. Some recipes used by the family are over one hundred and twenty years old, such as the caramelised roast almonds with vanilla. They also create nougat with their almonds, cooking in copper kettles with local lavender honey. The recipe is a very old one from nearby Montélimar.

Milk chocolate.

●Sweet ●Milk ●Cocoa 40% ●Sour ●Bitter

Taste Vanilla fudge; toffee; cream; roast; wood; pear; hazelnut; malt; barley; sunflower seed; honey, chocolate. Hint of coffee and molasses.

Lait Bolvie Sauvage
48%

Chocolaterie A. Morin ⊗ ⊗

Robust notes of roasted cacao fused with malt, wholesome molasses and especially tender dark sugar combine to create broad range of rich flavours. A drop of cream adds a luxurious touch. As the experience comes to a finish, slightly dry dark chocolate notes emerge. **Cacao** Harvested from wild trees in Bolivia. **Interestingly** Cacao trees are either cultivated, feral or wild. Cultivated trees (planted and then maintained by man) are the easiest to classify because the cultivator will be present, but cultivated trees may also be recognised by evidence of man's influence. For example, they may have been planted in some order, or they may have been pruned to grow in a distinctive Y shape. Another giveaway is that the trees may be trimmed to restrict their height to 3-4m to facilitate harvesting, inspection and maintenance. Feral cacao trees are cultivated trees that have been abandoned and are no longer maintained by man. Wild cacao trees are those which have occurred naturally, along with any previous generations on site, without deliberate intervention from man. Scientists can not always be certain if the cacao trees they discover on expeditions into remote forests are wild or feral. Even if the trees appear to be dispersed in a natural disorder, it is necessary to look for more confirmation of no intervention by man. The age of the cacao tree can be compared with that of the plants surrounding it to decide if the area was once cleared for cultivation and historical or archaeological evidence of human settlements can be sought.

Milk chocolate.

●●Sweet   ●●Butter   ●●Cocoa 48%   ●●Milk
●Bitter

Taste Wood; roast coffee; molasses; malt; barley; biscuit; toffee; cream; dark chocolate cake. Hint of nut, lemon rind and orange rind.

MADAGASCAR LAIT

Chocolaterie A. Morin ✤

An introduction of calm, smooth sunflower seed progresses on to comforting tastes of cream fudge and chocolate brownie. They are enriched and made more engaging by extraordinary sweet, acidic fruity details. **Cacao** Trinitario from Madagascar. **Pictured** Franck Morin inspects a cultivated cacao tree with a grower in Peru. As may be seen, the leaves of the tree grow abundantly. They are attached alternately to opposite sides of the branch by a short stalk. The largest leaves can measure over 15 inches long and their upper surface is almost glossy, as if lacquered. The underside is matt. Developing leaves, which hang vertically, may be pallid or red flushed. Mature leaves remain green all year. They are pointed, and take the form of a long and slim, or wide and full, ellipse or oval. Several rare varieties have been found with round leaves that are not pointed. The leaf edge can be smooth, gently undulate or, in rare cases, be serrated. Fallen leaves are left on the ground, they provide a humid and shaded habitat essential for the midges that pollinate the flowers of the cacao tree.

Milk chocolate.

●●Sweet ●●Milk ●●Butter ●●Cocoa ●Sour

Taste Sunflower seed; olive; ripe banana; chocolate; malt; Brazil nut; cream fudge; candied lime. Hint of salt, coffee, grapefruit, mango and candied cherry.

CHOCOLATERIE A. MORIN CACAOFÉVIER WWW.CHOCOLATERIE-MORIN.COM

A particularly flavoursome sweetness and delicious tangy cacao distinguish this lower percentage milk chocolate. Perhaps chocolate cake and cream or malted chocolate confections will spring to mind, but then you will become distracted by another aspect of the long-lasting complexity. There is plenty to enjoy and consider for those who like a sweeter fine chocolate. **Cacao** A blend of several origins. **Pictured** Mme Morin's collection of antique chocolate moulds are on display in the shop for visitors to view. The average chocolate mould is just a few inches tall, but a small number of exceptionally large pieces, like the one above, were produced to make spectacular figures for window displays.

Milk chocolate.

●●●Sweet   ●●Milk   ●●Butter   ●Cocoa 35%

Taste Molasses; malt; chocolate cake; cream; wholemeal toast; tamarind; hazelnut; sultana; apricot kernel. Hint of allspice, honeydew melon and flower.

LAIT
Chocolaterie A Morin ✽

WWW.CHOCOLATERIE-MORIN.COM

CHOCOLATERIE A MORIN   CACAOFÉVIER

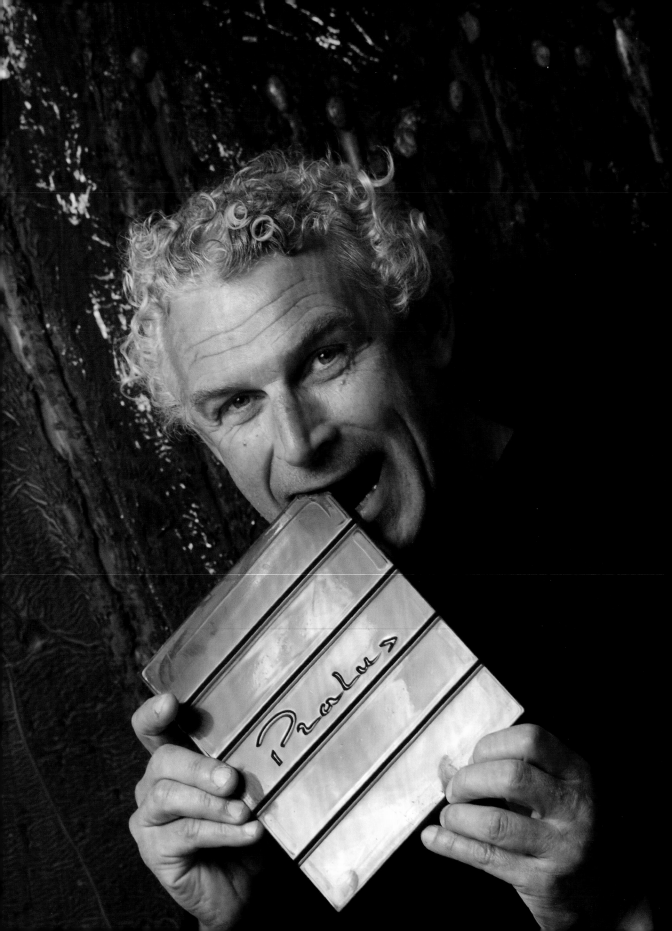

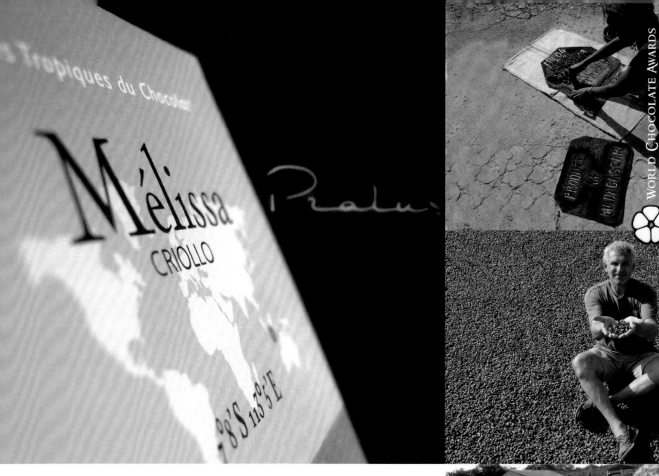

MÉLISSA

Pralus ✿✿✿

Chocolate alchemy: rich, dense chocolate with unforgettable rounded flavours and unexcessive highlights of juicy berries. Perfectly balanced. **Pralus say** Mélissa has lots of aficionados because it is so well balanced and striking for its flavours of vanilla, caramel, sweet and acidic spices. **Cacao** Criollo from the Pralus plantation (right) on the island of Nosy Be, situated on the North West coast of Madagascar. **Established** By August Pralus, who opened a pastry shop in Roanne's centre in 1948. It is still there today. François (pictured) followed in his father's footsteps, and whilst training at Bernachon, "it suddenly dawned on me that I could make my own chocolate from cocoa beans." Now his factory with fifty employees, also in Roanne, produces near to one hundred tonnes of chocolate from beans annually. It also produces many other sweet and savoury delicacies. **Made** In Roanne, located 55 miles North West of Lyon. **Pictured** Right: drying the cacao beans in the sun takes several days. They are turned over several times to ensure an even result.

Milk chocolate.

●●●Cocoa ●●Sweet ●●Milk ●Butter ●Vanilla ●Sour ●Bitter

Taste Molasses; tahini; yeast; olive; walnut; blue and red berry; caramel; ripe banana; wheat; vanilla fudge.

BARRE INFERNALE LAIT
Pralus ✦ ✦ ✦

This large, thick bar is as strong and charismatic on the inside as the outer. Complex, flavoursome and balanced, this is a feast rich in cacao. Hints of red (perhaps berries) and gorgeous brown flavours (perhaps fig, malt and molasses). The occasional roasted hazelnut surprises and delights. **Pralus say** A sensational creation by François Pralus, this bar is a praliné with toasted Piedmont hazelnuts and coated with milk chocolate 45% cocoa. "Diabolical!" **Cacao** Criollo from Pralus' 27ha plantation on the island of Nosy Be, off Madagascar. **Interestingly** "In order to get a precise idea of the flavours," François says, as he reveals one of his little secrets, "I infuse the cocoa in water that I lightly sugar, and leave it to settle. This way, I can have a clear idea of the flavours before setting production in motion." Below: the Praluline, created by Pralus in 1955. A rich brioche flavoured with pieces of cracked pralines made in-house from Valencia almonds and Piedmont hazelnuts coated in rose sugar.

Milk chocolate Blended with roasted hazelnut, almond and vanilla. Containing sparsely scattered whole hazelnuts.

●●●Cocoa ●●Hazelnut ●●Sweet ●●Butter ●Milk ●Vanilla ●Sour ●Bitter

Taste Molasses; fig, malt; red and blue berry; lemon and orange peel; tahini; yeast; walnut; caramel; ripe banana; vanilla fudge.

PRALUS CACAOFÉVIER WWW.CHOCOLATS-PRALUS.COM

Yuzu Macha

Henri Le Roux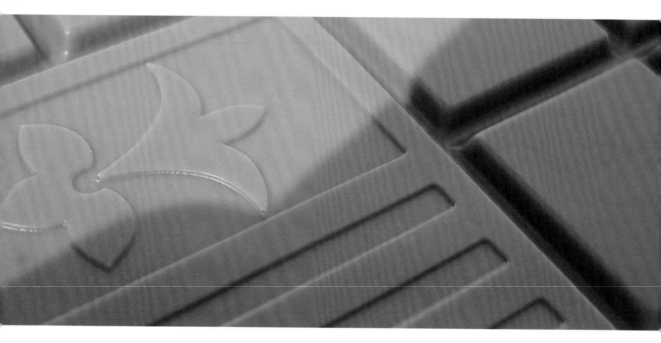

A harmony between the clean creaminess of milk and the pronounced sweet, sour and savoury notes of tea and fruit. The balance between each of the elements is consistent until the last moment, when the milk fades away and the tea flourishes leaving a slightly dry taste. **Le Roux say** A delicate agreement between the finesse of the macha (green tea from Japan) and the tangy sweetness of the yuzu (a Japanese citrus). **Established** In Quiberon, Brittany in 1977. Le Roux had worked as an apprentice in his parents' pastry shop and studied at the Coba school of pastry and chocolate in Basel, Switzerland before opening his shop. Le Roux, now retired, is best known for his caramel au beurre salé (salted butter caramels) also known as "C.B.S.," a name which he registered the rights to. Henri was also passionate about creating ice creams and chocolates. **Made In** Landévant, Brittany. The factory has a shop and offers tours by appointment. **Interestingly** Le Roux produce Yuzu Macha ice cream. **Pictured** Julien Gouzien, chief chocolatier.

White chocolate Blended with macha tea and yuzu powder.

●●Yuzu & Macha   ●●Milk   ●●Butter   ●Sweet   ●Sour   ●Dry

Taste Cream; lime pith; lime ice cream; grass; pine sap; green tea; apricot. Hint of bergamot, cinnamon; sultana and red grapefruit.

HENRI LE ROUX · WWW.CHOCOLATEROUX.EU

LAIT GOURMAND
Saldac ✿ ✿ ✿

A special chocolate because of its balance of fragrant fruit, tangy malt and creamy chocolate fudge notes. The result is engaging and refreshing, with both sweet and sour notes to relish. **Saldac say** A grand cru [prestigious harvest from a specific area] with milk. Very tender and aromatic, with notes of citrus fruits. **Cacao** Organic criollo from the Pangoa co-operative, Satipo province, located in the central Amazon rainforest of Peru. **Established** Saldac was created in 2000 in Montélimar, Drôme, France. It conducts ethical trade with various producers in Peru's remote rural areas, "outside the monopoly of the local intermediaries who offer prices so low that they only cover the cost of production." **Made** In the Drôme, France. "We work with an artisan chocolatier who brings great care to every stage of processing. The master chocolatier, thanks to his knowledge, transmitted over several generations, ensures a finished product of exceptional quality, with a well developed aroma." **Pictured** Left: the cacao tree's flower, which grows into a pod containing beans, reaching maturity within five months of fertilisation. Right: the Peruvian Amazon is part of the region in which the cacao tree is believed to have originated. It can still be found growing wild.

Milk chocolate.

●●Sweet ●●Milk ●●Butter ●●Cocoa 40% ●●Sour ●Bitter

Taste Ripe banana; pear; kiwi; lime candy; yellow grapefruit; malt; treacle; cream and chocolate fudge; hazelnut; tobacco. Hint of salt and brandy.

LAIT AU CAFÉ
Saldac ✿✿✿

Aromatic coffee shares the spotlight considerably with the creamy chocolate fudge, malt and fruit notes. Only the nutty aspects of the original chocolate are replaced by the fine coffee, allowing it to fit very naturally with the other flavours. Bold yet balanced, with complex and original flavours to appreciate. **Saldac say** An excellent marriage of coffee, milk and cocoa, worthy of a delicious cappuccino. With a pleasing deep flavour. **Cacao** Organic criollo from the Pangoa co-operative, Satipo province, central Amazon rainforest, Peru. **Interestingly** This organic coffee is grown at an elevation of up to 1750 metres above sea level in El Palomar, in the province of Chanchamayo, in Peru's Central Andes. Coffee accounts for ninety percent of the inhabitants' revenue. Photos: coffee berries (also called cherries), which grow green and turn amber then red as they mature, contain edible sweet flesh around the bean. It tastes a little like Red Bull. The berries must be picked individually by hand, with a twist. If pulled, they are unlikely to grow back again.

Milk chocolate. Blended with ground coffee.

●●Cocoa 40% ●●Sour ●●Sweet ●●Milk
●●Coffee 4% ●Bitter ●Butter

Taste Coffee; ripe banana; pear; kiwi; lime candy; yellow grapefruit; malt; treacle; cream and chocolate fudge; tobacco. Hint of brandy.

GERMANY

Republica Dominicana Bourbon Vanille

Coppeneur ✿ ✿ ✿

The sweet scent of vanilla wafts through the air as you open the wrapper. The vanilla-speckled chocolate is a sweet, rich, and indulgently creamy masterpiece. Complex for a white, because of its full-bodied dairy notes, nutty hints and caramel qualities, Dominican is also well-balanced, adding to the impression of completeness. **Coppeneur say** Enchanting. Gloriously creamy milk aromas harmonising with a strongly flavoursome malt; this corresponds to the cocoa character typical of the region. Pleasantly mellow but not sweet. Melting delicately, the intense taste spreads with the fresh Bourbon vanilla which determines the enjoyment of the finish. **Cacao** Organic trinitario from the Dominican Republic. **Established** In 1993 by Georg Bernardini, who left in 2010, and Oliver Coppeneur. **Made** In Bad Honnef. **Pictured** Coppeneur's shop in Bonn serves ice cream and hot or cold drinks made with this white chocolate. Top right: jars of spirits which may be added to drinks.

White chocolate Blended with vanilla.

●●●Milk ●●Vanilla ●●Sweet ●●Butter

Taste Mascarpone; honeydew melon; vanilla; caramel; sugar; butter; peanut.

coppeneur
chocolatier

[tchocolat]

coppeneur.

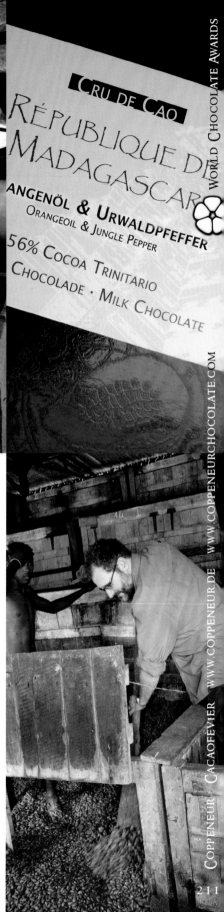

CRU DE CAO

RÉPUBLIQUE DE MADAGASCAR

ANGENÖL & URWALDPFEFFER
ORANGEOIL & JUNGLE PEPPER

56% COCOA TRINITARIO

CHOCOLADE · MILK CHOCOLATE

ORANGENÖL & URWALDPFEFFER

Coppeneur ⊛

Inside this black box are the gentle, sophisticated, Doctor Jekyll and the fiery Mister Hyde. Intense bursts of heat from the innocent-looking white peppercorns make this one of the hottest chocolate bars around, once it gets going. A soothing contrast is provided by gentle orange oil and a smooth, flavoursome chocolate. This bar perpetually fades between the two characters as you eat, allowing you to enjoy one, a fusion of both, then the other. **Coppeneur say** Exciting! Intense cocoa flavours melt tenderly, accompanied by fresh orange oil, giving a feeling of relaxation. A spontaneous awakening follows as you bite a white peppercorn. **Cacao** Organic trinitario from North Madagascar. **Pictured** After the cacao pods are gathered, the process of cutting them open and removing the beans starts. The raw beans are in an edible white pulp which has a sweet taste, similar to lychee. The wet beans are taken to the site of the stepped fermenting boxes and deposited at the top. The beans are turned and shovelled down into a fresh box periodically to ensure an even fermentation.

Milk chocolate Blended with vanilla and orange oil. Scattered on one side with whole white peppercorns.

●●●Hot ●●●Cocoa 56% ●●Orange ●Milk ●Sweet ●Vanilla ●Butter ●Bitter

Taste Mild peppercorn; hot peppercorn; roast; papaya; cream; milk; toasted wholemeal bread; molasses; tahini; raisin. Hint of lemon rind, fig and nut.

Zimt
& Kakaonibs

Coppeneur ✿ ✿

For lovers of the suave nutty taste of Coppeneur's Ecuadorian cocoa as much as it is for fans of mellow cinnamon. Presented with fresh-tasting creamy milk, the fabulous cocoa is the principal to which tasty cinnamon adds more complexity, and a gentle warmth. The nibs are small, to be enjoyed simultaneously with the chocolate. **Coppeneur say** The highly aromatic and full-bodied nacional cocoa is the foundation of this specialty. Its strong points are gently rounded by the milk. Thus the pure flavour of the broken nibs of fresh-roasted cacao beans can be expressed. The accompaniment of fine spicy Ceylon cinnamon creates a harmonious interplay of fine flavours. **Cacao** Nacional, grown organically in Ecuador.

Milk chocolate Blended with cinnamon and vanilla. Scattered on one side with cocoa nibs.

●●●Cocoa 55%　　●●●Milk 24%
●●Vanilla　　●●Butter　　●Sweet
●Cinnamon　●Bitter

Taste Whole milk; tea; roast; malt; tahini; cinnamon; cashew; butter. Hint of honey and treacle.

WWW.COPPENEURCHOCOLATE.COM

WWW.COPPENEUR.DE

Coppeneur. Cacao Février.

213

HOLUNDERBLÜTEN
Coppeneur ✿ ✿

Luscious, creamy milk and a stout "no frills" cocoa prove great flavours to add to the magic of sensitive and aromatic elderflower. The finely chopped flowers merge seamlessly, contributing complex flavours gently, to complete this chocolate. **Coppeneur say** Spring feelings. In a lively and restless fashion, like the flitting of bees and butterflies on a field of flowers, the elder blossoms play with the aromas of this mellow chocolate. Here they find a platform on which its entire flavour can completely unfurl. They endow the finish with a rich diversity of floral impressions. **Interestingly** Above: holes in the tray allow the chocolate truffle shells to be filled before they are finished with more chocolate and then icing sugar, inside the rotating copper coating pan. Copper is traditionally used because its ability to conduct and distribute heat evenly.

Milk chocolate Blended with vanilla. Sparsely scattered on one side with minute pieces of elderflower.

●●Milk   ●●Cocoa 57%   ●●Elderflower   ●Sweet   ●Vanilla   ●Butter   ●Bitter

Taste Deep roast; chocolate cake; chocolate mousse; whole milk; cream; tobacco; almond. Hint of tahini and lemon rind.

KARAMELL & FLOR DE SAL

Coppeneur ⊗ ⊗

This is the dark side of creamy milk chocolate, for those who love a thoroughly roasted, dusky, flavour. The twilight theme is enriched by the deep, dark aspects of treacle toffee and enhanced by gentle salt. The additions are remarkable because they are flavoursome, without contributing sharp saltiness or saturating sweetness. Neither is the harmony influenced by butter, sugar or vanilla flavours. **Coppeneur say** Mellow creamy milk aromas join malty and caramel cocoa tones to form the body of this chocolate. Golden baked sugar and Mediterranean sea salt further enhance the body and taste experience. The finish is then determined by pleasant malt and flower tones. **Cacao** Organic trinitario, from the Dominican Republic. **Pictured** Opposite page: the cacao tree flower grows not only from the branches, but also from the trunk. It is about 1-2cm in diameter and is pollinated by a midge so small it could fly through the eye of a needle. The midge lives for only ten days.

Milk chocolate Blended with caramel and salt.

●●Cocoa 52%   ●●Milk 24%   ●●Caramel   ●Sweet   ●Bitter   ●Butter

Taste Whole milk; salt; nut; deep roast; wholemeal toast; treacle; malt. Hint of dried date and fig.

RÉPUBLIQUE DE MADAGASCAR

Coppeneur ✹ ✹

This super-smooth chocolate is complex and tangy. Gentle hints of toast and tropical fruit emerge from its suave nutty and creamy character. **Coppeneur say** Very expressive. Mild fruit, an impression of papaya and mango, are typical characteristics of this cocoa. They re-emerge here. Finely embedded and rounded off in a composition of milk and vanilla, but they assert themselves clearly and enduringly. **Cacao** Trinitario. Organically grown in North Madagascar. **Interestingly** Known as the Red Island because of its rusty coloured soil, Madagascar is the world's fourth largest island. It is twice the size of mainland Great Britain.

Milk chocolate Blended with vanilla.

●●●Cocoa 56%　　●●Milk 24%
●●Butter　　●●Vanilla　　●Sweet
●Sour　●Bitter

Taste Roast; papaya; tahini; mango; creamy milk; molasses; toasted wholemeal bread; raisin; bee wax. Hint of lemon rind, fig, nut, smoke and aniseed.

REPÚBLICA DEL ECUADOR

Coppeneur ✪ ✪ ✪

A smooth, creamy chocolate with tremendously tasty cocoa. Its distinct, lingering, nutty, seedy and malted hues are gently enhanced by the rich milk, tantalising sweetness, and the spice from a touch of vanilla. A great example of the remarkable qualities of cacao nacional - and Coppeneur. **Coppeneur say** Full-bodied and self-assured, it embodies the originality and uniqueness of the nacional cocoa. Starting with an impression of fruits of the forest, vanilla combines harmoniously with discreet transitions, with cinnamon and nuts. Its intense aroma has a slight tendency towards burnt clay and precious woods. **Cacao** Organically grown nacional, from Ecuador. **Interestingly** Coppeneur's principal sources of cacao in the Los Rios province of Ecuador, Hacienda Iara (pictured) and Iara II, are named after one of the daughters of owner Gonzalo Martinetti (left).

Milk chocolate Blended with vanilla.

●●●Cocoa 55%　●●●Milk　●●Vanilla　●●Butter　●Sweet

Taste Brown bread; mascarpone; malt; violet; almond; Brazil nut; walnut; toasted seeds; tahini; honey; golden syrup. Hint of lemon.

221

WILD COCOA DE AMAZONAS 45%

Hachez ✸

A smooth, creamy, chocolate that will gently reveal a remarkable range of sweet, mild and medium dark cocoa notes. **Hachez say** Cocoa-intense chocolate. Stimulating by virtue of the mid tangy cocoa flavour. The gentle sweetness is wrapped harmoniously in a delicate smoothness and discreet shades of cocoa. Wild Cocoa de Amazonas grows in the rainforest in its natural environment, according to nature's designs. Its fruits are smaller than usual, but the flavour and aroma they contain are more intense and stronger. It is comparable to the difference between strawberries grown in the fields or in the woods. Wild Cocoa underlines the expertise of Hachez as a specialist in cocoa products. **Cacao** Harvested from trees growing wild in the Amazon rainforest. **Established** July 1890 by Joseph Emile Hachez, a chocolatier of Belgian origin, who created a delicate recipe to manufacture fine chocolates. The recipe is still honoured and the headquarters of this family owned company have remained in Westerstrasse, in the heart of Bremen to this day. **Made** In Bremen.

Milk chocolate Blended with vanilla.

●●●Butter ●●Cocoa 45% ●●Sweet ●●Milk ●Vanilla

Taste Honeydew melon; sunflower seed; liquorice; honey; malt; chocolate mousse; vanilla cream. Hint of molasses.

HACHEZ CACAOFÉVIER WWW.HACHEZ.DE

223

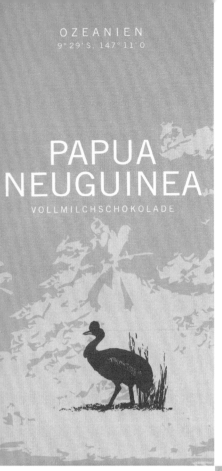

PAPUA NEUGUINEA

VOLLMILCHSCHOKOLADE

A smooth and sweet chocolate that holds exceptional and curious cocoa flavours. **Meybona say** A strong taste with a distinct bitter note. Our series of Origins Chocolates is made from exquisite cocoa beans from the respective regions, carefully manufactured into finest chocolate. **Cacao** Trinitario from Papua New Guinea. **Established** In 1923 by Emil and Luise Meyerkamp to manufacture sweets, chocolates and jellies. Today their two daughters and grandson run the company. **Made** In Löhne. **Interestingly** In 1526, Portugese captain Don Jorge de Meneses accidentally came upon Papua New Guinea's principal island. He named it by using a Malay word: "Ilhas dos Papuas" or "Land of the Fuzzy-haired People." Subsequently in 1545 Spanish explorer Inigo Ortiz de Retes added "New Guinea" because he saw a resemblance between the islands' inhabitants and those of the African Guinea coast. Cacao was introduced to the island in 1880 by German traders and exportation began in 1905. Cacao cultivation only became widespread when the Australian administration promoted it to villagers in the 1950's. It is estimated that over a million people now depend on cacao for their livelihood and around forty thousand tonnes cocoa are produced annually. **Pictured** The cassowary is native to the rainforests of New Guinea. The flightless bird is the largest in the world after the ostrich. It stands up to 2m tall. It has a sturdy yet slightly flexible "casque" on top of its head. No one really knows for sure why cassowaries have casques.

Milk chocolate Blended with vanilla.

●●●Cocoa 45%   ●●●Sweet   ●●Milk   ●●Butter   ●●Vanilla

Taste Honeydew melon; pecan; cashew; sesame; malt; cinnamon.

Papua Neuguinea
Meybona ✵✵

CACAOFEVIER · WWW.MEYBONA.DE

MEYBONA   CACAOFEVIER

Meybona

Meybona

Feinste Schokoladen!

Kakaobohnen
Elfenbein

225

GUÁCIMO

Rausch ✪

A smooth, elegant chocolate with tender, aromatic cocoa. The creamy milk and sophisticated caramel sensations are mellowed by a generous proportion of butter. **Rausch say** Enjoy the richness of nuances in taste that makes Plantagen Schokolade so unique. It has a full aroma and still is amazingly mild; every single variety is carefully balanced to bring out the character of its cocoa. Traditionally, Costa Rica grows excellent fine flavoured cocoa. It is especially suited for dark milk chocolate like the Guácimo plantation chocolate. **Cacao** Trinitario from the Guácimo plantation, East Costa Rica. **Made** In Peine, near Hannover, Germany. **Established** In 1918 in Berlin by Wilhelm Rausch, himself the son of a chocolatier and confectioner. He produced gingerbread, chocolate bars and chocolates. Today, Rausch remains a family business: three children continue the tradition.

Milk chocolate.

●●●Butter   ●●Milk 18%   ●●Cocoa 47%   ●●Sweet

Taste Crème caramel; honey; allspice; avocado; milk; gentle roast. Hint of coffee and hazelnut.

WEISSE DAMEN

Sarotti ✿ ✿ ✿

Weisse Damen means White Lady, but Vanilla Queen is more appropriate. It is a huge hit because of its incomparably vivid vanilla, enrobed in sumptuous cream and tender sweet sugar. **Sarotti say** Extra smooth and creamy. Tender aromatic white chocolate made with the finest bourbon vanilla. Weisse Damen is a special experience for the fastidious connoisseur. **Established** In Berlin on September the 16th, 1852. The confectionary company was producing chocolate by 1883. Sarotti is now part of the Stollwerck group. **Made** In Germany. **Interestingly** The magician from the Arabian One Thousand and One Nights has been Sarotti's trademark for one hundred years. The idea was inspired by the fact that Sarotti was originally located on Moor Street in Berlin and that the character reminds us of the fantastic side of chocolate that enchants us since childhood. **Pictured** Vanilla is the only orchid to provide edible fruit. It is a jungle vine that climbs along tree trunks, or other supports, attached by its roots. It can grow to over 100ft long. It flowers once a year, at dawn, for only a few hours, and falls from the vine the next day, unless it is pollinated. Both vanilla and its pollinator, the melipona stingless bee, are native to Mexico and Guatemala. The bee seems to be made for the orchid: it knows that to access the pollen it must push open a flap, which obstructs other pollinators. Although Hernán Cortés brought vanilla to Europe during the Spanish conquest of the 1520's, it was not possible to cultivate it as a crop outside Central America for three hundred years. The bee's secret was discovered in 1836 by Belgian Charles Morren, and in 1841, Edmond Albius, a twelve year old slave, who lived on the French island of Bourbon (now Réunion) in the Indian Ocean, conceived a practical method for hand pollination. Vanilla pods take five months to grow. After harvest, a curing process ferments and dries them, while retaining essential oils.

White chocolate Blended with vanilla.

●●●Vanilla   ●●●Sweet   ●●●Milk   ●●Butter 30%

Taste Whole milk; honey; vanilla cream; custard; caramel. Hint of caramel and flour.

SAROTTI CACAOFÈVIER WWW.SCHWARZE-HERREN.SCHOKOLADE.DE

WHITE CRISP CHOCOLATE

Vivani ✿ ✿

This special recipe brings together complex sweet, dairy and savoury flavours with a refreshing touch of sourness from yoghurt. Well balanced and tangy, with pleasing crisp and tender textures from puffed rice. **Vivani say** A creamy white chocolate with a light rice crisp filling. Mild and creamy for sweet-toothed munchers! **Made** From the beans in the Ludwig Weinrich factory, Herford, Germany. **Established** In 2000 by Andreas Meyer (above). Vivani is a brand of EcoFinia, a subsidiary of Ludwig Weinrich. Vivani chocolate is distributed in around fifty countries. **Interestingly** The paintings featured on Vivani's boxes are the work of artist - and chocolate lover - Annette Wessel. Vivani explain the collaborative project as, "chocolate wrapped in art! In our opinion, sensual pleasures and art are the two foundation stones on which the Mediterranean way of life is built. Art speaks all languages. It exerts the same fascination all over the world - just like good chocolate. Our idea is to use the art of chocolate to create a total work of art for the delight of art lovers and gourmets alike."

White chocolate Blended with vanilla and yoghurt. Containing small crisp malted puffed rice.

●●●Vanilla   ●●Milk 27%   ●●Sweet   ●●Yoghurt   ●●Malt   ●●Butter 27%   ●Rice

Taste Vanilla; caramel; malt; cream; natural yoghurt. Hint of salt.

GUATEMALA

DANTA CHOCOLATE

WWW.DANTACHOCOLATE.COM

FINCA LOS UJUXTES
Danta Chocolate ✇

Sweet and chocolaty with plenty of character to enjoy from the rounded mid-range notes. **Danta say** Classic flavours. Great notes of caramel and coffee. **Cacao** Predominantly trinitario, from Finca Los Ujuxtes, San Antonio, in Suchitepéquez, south west Guatemala (pictured left). The saplings were brought from Costa Rica, before the 1979 blight. **Established** In 2008 in Guatemala City by Carlos Eichenberger, who began the business by selling his chocolate creations online and to friends. In December of 2009 Danta's shop opened, complete with interior windows to provide customers with a view into the workshop. **Made** In Zone fourteen, Guatemala City, Guatemala.

Milk chocolate Blended with vanilla.

••Cocoa 39% ••Sweet ••Milk ••Vanilla ••Butter

Taste Malt; molasses; roast; coffee; caramel; almond; cream; hazelnut.

Finca Los Ujuxtes Guatemala

Milk

FINCA LAS ACACIAS

Danta Chocolate ⊛ ⊛

Acacias captivates you with its playful sweet and (slightly) sour citrus flavours. This vivacious chocolate also holds complex caramel and lavish cream notes. **Danta say** Las Acacias tastes stronger than its cocoa percentage indicates. Fruity and potent, with red berry and mild citrus. It is also very popular amongst those who make drinking chocolate, as a little goes a long way. **Cacao** Criollo and trinitario, from Finca las Acacias, Escuintla region, south Guatemala. **Interestingly** Danta means tapir: the long snouted, metre tall mammal is native to the jungles of Central and South America. We were advised by a Maya friend never to run, but to, "dodge to the side, if a danta ever comes your way. They have no steering, no reverse, and no brakes!" Danta is also the name of arguably the largest known pyramid of the Maya world, located in the El Mirador archaeological site, northern Petén, near Tikal (pictured). The step pyramids were once painted in a bright red-orange mineral pigment (see Danta's wrappers). These were important sites for chocolate consumption during the Maya empire's one thousand year reign.

Milk chocolate Blended with vanilla.

●●Cocoa 39%   ●●Sweet   ●●Milk   ●●Vanilla   ●●Butter   ●Bitter

Taste Cranberry; caramel; bonfire toffee; butterscotch; cream; hint of yellow grapefruit. Hint of herbs.

Finca Las Acacias Guatemala

DANTA CHOCOLATE

BLANCO
Danta Chocolate ✣

Sweet and mellow flavours with interesting details. A careful balance of milk, sweetness and vanilla makes this a great white. **Cacao** Mainly trinitario, exclusively from Finca Los Ujuxtes, San Antonio, Suchitepéquez, Guatemala. **Interestingly** Danta use whole vanilla pods in their milk chocolate, and vanilla seeds in the white. These vanilla orchids are grown organically in the cloud forest highlands of Cobán, in central Guatemala. This lush region receives more than seventy inches of rain per year, and is renowned for its wild orchids and gourmet coffee. Danta's founder Carlos Eichenberger, who learnt his craft in Italy and France (including at Valrhona's École du Grand Chocolat) describes his approach to roasting cacao as minimalist. "I try to roast only until the moisture and acid are evaporated and the husk comes off easily." He typically roasts beans for around six minutes at a higher temperature, followed by twenty five at a lower setting. **Pictured** Antigua Guatemala, in Suchitepéquez. The former capital was once one of the great cities of the Spanish empire. It is surrounded by three volcanoes and many Maya communities, each identified by their clothing's unique colour, figures and weave. Below: dried cacao beans (between the jars) on sale in the market are used for ritual or culinary purposes. Atole is the most popular drink: ground corn flour stirred with boiling water and flavoured with cacao, cinnamon or sugar. It is served steaming hot (left).

White chocolate Blended with vanilla.

●●●Butter 37%   ●●Sweet   ●●Milk   ●●Vanilla

Taste Flour; cream; honey; salt; custard.

CHOCOLATE BLANCO
◆ DANTA CHOCOLATE
CHOCOLATE BLANCO

BLANCO CON TROCITOS
Danta Chocolate ✪

Astonishing flavours emerge from this speckled chocolate which is paradoxically both dark and light. The roasted cocoa taste is tempered by the sweetness, resulting in a tasty, dynamic, fusion of flavours. **Danta say** The finest and most carefully processed Guatemalan cacao, which we transform with great care and patience into fine chocolate. **Interestingly** Danta's logo was designed by Carlos' niece Ana Cristina Galvez, a graphic designer who now lives in California and works in the entertainment industry. The logo was inspired by the cross-section of a cacao pod and styled so that the beans inside resemble a Mayan pyramid. **Cacao** Mostly trinitario, exclusively from Finca Los Ujuxtes, San Antonio, in Suchitepéquez, south west Guatemala.

White chocolate Blended with vanilla. Containing cocoa nibs.

●●Cocoa ●●Sweet ●●Butter 37% ●●Milk ●●Vanilla

Taste Flour; cream; mint; coffee; tea; roast. Hint of egg nog and stracciatella gelato.

ITALY

Toscano White

Amedei ✿ ✿

Pleasure comes in the form of dreamy vanilla-kissed dairy notes and joyful sweetness. These sensational sweet flavours have depth too. **Amedei say** A concentration of sweetness, pleasant and creamy flavours, leaving a delightful sensation of fresh milk on the palate. With an aroma and flavour like no other, it is both delicate and powerful. **Established** In 1998 by Cecilia Tessieri and her brother Alessio, who had made pralines in their own workshop since 1990. **Made** In La Rotta, near Pontedera, Tuscany. **Interestingly** Cecilia named Amedei after the surname of her maternal grandmother.

White chocolate Blended with vanilla.

●●●Sweet   ●●Milk   ●●Butter 29%   ●●Vanilla

Taste Vanilla; whipped cream; honey; golden syrup; egg nog; butter; flour; caramel; dulce de leche. Hint of potato and salt.

TOSCANO
WHITE

AMEDEI
TUSCANY

CIOCCOLATO AL LATTE
Bianco

AMEDEI CACAOFÈVIER   WWW.AMEDEI.COM

CIOCCOLATO BIANCO CON PISTACCHI

Amedei ✿ ✿

Here we have a delicious gastronomic dessert with complex flavours to appreciate. The aromas of freshly-roasted pistachio have literally been captured in this white chocolate, which possesses both sweetness and substance. **Amedei say** It takes courage to break away from the crowd. That's what we've done, merging white chocolate with the superior taste and aroma of green Bronte pistachios from Sicily. The sensational taste more than repays this daring combination, a fusion of flavours, with both seeking to be strongest. And they blend perfectly in the aftertaste. **Interestingly** Sicily is the only Italian region where pistachios can be grown. Here the land has been fertilised by Etna's lava and volcanic ashes, which produces small nuts of a superior taste. Although eighty percent of the land in Bronte's commune is dedicated to cultivating pistachios, it represents only one percent of world production.

White chocolate Blended with vanilla. Containing pistachio nibs.

●●●Sweet   ●●Milk   ●●Butter 29%   ●●Pistachio   ●Vanilla

Taste Vanilla cream; ricotta; flour; lightly roasted pistachio; golden syrup; caramel; potato. Hint of cashew.

TOSCANO BROWN

Amedei ✿ ✿ ✿

A remarkable blend of chocolaty cocoa that includes an equally sophisticated blend of creamy milk. Toscano Brown strikes a rare, almost magical, balance: satisfying in terms of cocoa, dairy and sweetness, yet it is easy to eat. Its flavours are also well-rounded, without any domineering notes, yet it can sustain intrigue long-term with its great details which can be appreciated and deliberated. **Amedei say** An ode to childhood memories, made of an exclusive blend of milk. A real jewel among those available on the market, standing out because of its delicious flavours of butter, vanilla and honey, but never too sweet. **Pictured** A beautiful mural of cacao surrounds the entrance to Amedei's purpose built factory, situated in the Tuscan countryside. It is featured on the covers of several of their dark chocolate bars.

Milk chocolate Blended with vanilla.

●●Sweet   ●●Milk   ●●Cocoa 35%   ●●Butter   ●●Vanilla

Taste Vanilla; chocolate; ricotta; mascarpone; buffalo mozzarella; smoke; nut; pale sultana; barley; butter; tobacco.

Latte con Nocciole

Amedei

The simple name belies a sophisticated recipe. Each element in this fusion has special qualities: the fragrance of vanilla; elegant aromas of roasted hazelnut; tender cocoa. They are all carried on complex waves of milk and cream. **Amedei say** Legendary Amedei chocolate comes together with grand hazelnuts from the Piedmont region. Our version of this classic pairing is marked by its especially long finish. The sweetness of milk chocolate combines with the aroma of toasted hazelnuts to create a delectable sensation of freshness on the palate and an irresistible desire to try another bite. **Interestingly** Amedei use vanilla from a single plantation in Madagascar.

Milk chocolate Blended with vanilla. Containing hazelnut nibs.

●●Sweet ●●Milk ●●Butter ●●Vanilla ●●Cocoa 32% ●●Hazelnut

Taste Lightly roasted hazelnut; vanilla; cream; fine butter; chocolate; roast; condensed milk; whole milk. Hint of cheese.

tostino

Sgrama

Crema Toscana alla Nocciola

Amedei ✸ ✸ ✸

An exquisite fusion of the finest roast hazelnut with the finest milk chocolate, which has been tailor made to compliment it. Crema Toscana has pronounced, wide ranging, long lasting and tender notes of freshly roasted hazelnut. The blend of cacao is equally aromatic and tender. **Amedei say** Our hazelnut and cocoa creams are prepared with the highest quality ingredients just like all of Amedei's creations. Perfect as a spread at breakfast time, for preparing desserts or perhaps by the spoonful, reminding you of your favourite childhood treat. **Pictured** Cecilia Tessieri, the creative force behind Amedei.

Milk chocolate paste Blended with hazelnut paste and vanilla.

●●Cocoa ●●Hazelnut ●●Milk ●●Sweet ●●Butter ●Oil ●Vanilla

Taste Light roast hazelnut; milk; nut; condensed milk, sultana; fig. Hint of honey, caramel; malt; golden syrup and cinnamon.

QUADROTTI TOSCANI

Cioccolato al Latte Bianco con Ripieno
di Pistachi e Granella di Cacao
Amedei ✪

A sweet melody of vanilla and dreamy white
chocolate, with a delightful little crunch of cocoa.
The gentle aspects of hazelnut and pistachio add
to the dreaminess of the experience. **Amedei say**
White chocolate filled with pistachios and cocoa
nibs. This is a marriage of white and green: white
chocolate with vanilla flavour and pistachios from
Bronte, Sicily, finely chopped and made into a
paste. And just a touch of ground cocoa beans
like a light crunchy sprinkle, highlighting the
chocolate's sweet softness. Amedei's celebrated
know-how, when it comes to combining
ingredients, textures, flavours and aroma, runs
free in these exquisite filled chocolate squares.
Interestingly All cacao destined for Amedei's
chocolate travels "first class." It is refrigerated
during transit to the factory in Italy, then
transferred to Amedei's cooled storage room.

White chocolate Blended with vanilla. Filled
with pistachio and hazelnut paste, with minute
cocoa nibs.

●●●Sweet ●●●Butter ●●Milk ●●Hazelnut
●●Pistachio ●●Vanilla ●Cocoa

Taste Cream; custard; light chocolate; caramel;
malt; gentle roast hazelnut; gentle roast pistachio;
hazelnut spread. Hint of salt.

TOSCANO NUT BROWN GIANDUJA
Amedei ⊗ ⊗

Gentle, elegant and sophisticated are words that spring to mind when describing Amedei's interpretation of the classic Italian hazelnut chocolate. This is a smooth bar: the chocolate has been tailor-made to show off the soft, dreamy tones of almond and hazelnut. **Amedei say** A finely balanced taste in a classic chocolate that is slightly crunchy, fragrant and gratifying. **Interestingly** The hazelnuts used in this chocolate are Tonda Gentile delle Langhe (Round and Tender from Langhe) an area in the Piedmont region, north Italy). This variety is prized for its flavour and texture. Left: Cecilia, co-founder of Amedei, uses a guillotine cross-section cutter to evaluate fermented and dried cacao beans upon arrival at the factory. One hundred beans are placed into the spaces on one side of the metal box and the two hinged sides are locked shut. The long guillotine blade is pushed into a slot in one end of the box to slice the beans in half so that their condition can be visually inspected. The result is given as the percentage of good beans found.

Milk chocolate Blended with vanilla, hazelnut paste and almond paste.

●●●Butter ●●Cocoa 32% ●●Sweet ●●Milk
●●Hazelnut ●●Almond ●●Vanilla

Taste Roast hazelnut; roast almond; butter; hazelnut oil; chocolate; roast; cream; vanilla; caramel. Hint of salt and cinnamon.

QUADROTTI TOSCANI

Cioccolato al Latte e Crema
Toscana con Granella di
Nocciola
Amedei ✿ ✿ ✿

AMEDEI CACAOFÉVIER WWW.AMEDEI.COM

Amedei's "Tuscan Squares" are a careful composition of flavours and textures. The pleasure of complex milk chocolate and hazelnut tastes is enhanced by three textures: a slight crunch (cane sugar and hazelnut paste filling); a rich texture (hazelnut spread) and a smooth refined outer layer of chocolate. **Amedei say** Milk chocolate bar filled with Crema Toscana and nibbed hazelnuts. Crema Toscana is the feature player in a creamy wave of Gianduja, making the perfect home to fresh toasted Piedmont hazelnuts. Extremely fine milk chocolate that should be delicately bitten into for the first moment of an unforgettable encounter. Amedei's celebrated know-how, when it comes to combining ingredients, textures, flavours and aroma, runs free in these exquisite filled chocolate squares. These creations are an expansion on the concept of our praline, demonstrating once again the excellence of the chocolatier's skill. **Interestingly** For Amedei, who roast cacao beans in-house, it was part of their ethos to also install a nut roaster in the factory. The same control, care and knowledge is applied to the almonds, hazelnuts and pistachios found in their chocolates. Because they are used almost immediately, the inimitable aromas of freshly roasted nuts are captured in the recipes. Right: Crema Toscana.

Milk chocolate Blended with vanilla. Containing a hazelnut and milk chocolate paste filling with hazelnut nibs.

●●●Sweet ●●●Butter ●●Milk ●●Cocoa ●●Hazelnut ●Vanilla

Taste Light roast hazelnut; honey; caramel; chocolate; salt; cottage cheese; cream; buffalo mozzarella; smoke; pale sultana; barley; butter; tobacco.

259

BIANCOMENTA

Domori ⊗ ⊗ ⊗

Impossibly fresh and complex mint flavours make this bar a sensation. This smooth, creamy, dark-green chocolate attests to Domori's talent for selecting and preparing the most sublime ingredients. **Domori say** The smoothness of the white chocolate combined with real leaves of wild mint from Morocco that grows on the high grounds of the Atlas Mountains. Smooth and refreshing. **Interestingly** Two percent of Biancomenta (Whitemint) is Nanah mint. The leaf is also used in traditional North African tea: a sweet drink usually served after meals. **Established** In 1999 by Gianluca Franzoni. He had developed the idea during a three year stay in Venezuela, where his house, "ended up looking more like an alchemist's workshop than a home, as it was packed with cacao beans, pots, mixers, and an incalculable number of coffee-roasting drums." Gianluca chose the name Domori at this time. "I was living in cacao and coffee plantations, and wanted to choose an evocative name for the project, so I thought of Venice as a land of trade, spices and intellectual activity, and of the Two Moors [Do Mori] that are the two bronze statues on the clock tower in St Mark's Square, who for me metaphorically represent the two dark toasted beans of cocoa and coffee." **Made** In None, Turin. **Pictured** Domori's own plantation, Hacienda San José in Venezuela, a principal grower of rare criollo cacao.

White chocolate Blended with mint leaf.

●●●Mint ●●●Milk ●●●Sweet ●●Butter

Taste Fresh mint leaf; mascarpone; honey. Hint of black pepper.

BIANCOLIQUIRIZIA
Domori ✲ ✲ ✲

The most exquisite and aromatic flavours of liquorice root are the heart of this recipe. They are carried on creamy waves of pure-tasting white chocolate. Also notable is Biancoliquirizia's sweetness: moderate and sophisticated, like a wild flower honey. Lovers of liquorice may marvel at Domori's magical talent for incorporating fantastic, vivid ingredients into their delicacies. **Domori say** An unusual combination between white chocolate and Calabrian liquorice, which is recognised as the finest in the world. The result is a product that unleashes the fresh, long-lasting flavour of an extraordinary root. **Cacao** From Apurímac, Peru. **Interestingly** The word liquorice comes from its Greek name, Glycyrrhiza glabra, which means sweet root. This part of the tall shrub can be chewed or can have its sweet juice extracted. **Pictured** Founder Gianluca Franzoni among the jute sacks used for transporting cacao to the factory. The material is breathable but strong, making it ideal for agricultural products. Opposite: the stainless steel tubes are heated by water in order to melt large blocks of cocoa butter. Then ingredients are added to make white chocolate.

White chocolate Blended with liquorice root and vanilla.

●●●Liquorice ●●Sweet ●●Milk ●●Butter ●Vanilla

Taste Fresh liquorice root juice; sweet cream; honey; butter.

DOMORI

CACAO CULT

100% CACAO VENEZOLANO

cacao SAN JOSÉ
FRANCESCHI · 1830~
www.CacaoSanJose.com

WWW.DOMORI.COM

DOMORI   CACAOFÉVIER

263

Cappuccino

Domori ✿ ✿ ✿

An exquisite interpretation: milky white chocolate, with a clean, crisp, taste, which supports and emphasises the strength and distinctive flavours of the coffee. It is highly aromatic and detailed, with divine medium and deep-roasted flavours to savour. **Domori say** From coffee cup to chocolate bar: cappuccino is a wonderful adaptation of this most Italian of rituals. The delicate milky notes of the white chocolate serve to enhance the distinctive aroma of Illy coffee. A pleasure that will awaken your senses, just like a real cappuccino. **Interestingly** Cappuccino ("little hood") seems to be a reference to the pointed whip of foam often seen on top of the drink. The name has also been attributed to the similarity between the beverage's colour and that of the brown hooded robes of Capuchin Franciscan friars. **Pictured** Ripe cacao pods on Domori's plantation are carefully cut open in order to remove the beans without damaging them. If any beans are broken they are discarded. The beans are then piled into wood boxes to ferment. There is no specific season for harvesting cacao: it is a matter of walking through the plantation and hand-picking pods on a daily basis. The colour that indicates maturity is different for each variety.

White chocolate Blended with coffee.

●●●Coffee　●●●Milk　●●Sweet　●●Butter　●Bitter

Taste Coffee; milk; sugar cane. Hint of black pepper, tea and warm spice.

DOMORI CACAOFÈVIER   WWW.DOMORI.COM

JAVAGREY

Domori ✸

Javagrey showcases sophisticated dairy flavours. As the chocolate melts, it gives the sensation of a refined chocolate milkshake made with creamy, fresh, mountain milk. Pause for a moment and the subtle aromas of cocoa that underscore the gentle chocolate flavour emerge: tobacco, earth, hints of spice and plum. **Domori say** The smoked and slightly spicy hints of Java blond mixed with the sweetness of the milk from the grey cows of Tyrol. An unusual liaison between Indonesia and Austria. The step from the Alps to the shade of the volcanoes of the island of Java is shorter than it seems. **Cacao** Criollo from Java, Indonesia. Named "blond" because of the bean's rare fair colour. Above: Domori's "sensory chart" of its chocolates.

Milk Chocolate.

●●Cocoa 45%   ●●Sweet   ●●Milk   ●Butter

Taste Cream; mascarpone; wood; plum; hay; tobacco; earth; chocolate mousse.

LATTESAL
Domori ✲ ✲ ✲

The salt, milk and cocoa are delicate and complex, making this a highly refined harmony of tasty flavours. All the subtle details of each ingredient may be savoured. The texture is incredibly smooth. **Domori say** We chose the sweet and aromatic Guérande salt to bring forth a fresh hint of banana and citrus fruits from this fine milk chocolate. **Cacao** Arriba nacional from Ecuador. **Pictured** The Guérande sea salt used comes from marshes on France's Atlantic coast (right). It is naturally grey because it crystallises on clay, from which it takes its high trace element content. It is not refined or bleached. Guérande salt tastes less salty than many: it is softer on the palate and richer in flavour, with a faint sweetness to it.

Milk chocolate Blended with salt.

●●Salt 0.4%   ●●Cocoa 45%   ●●Sweet   ●●Milk   ●Butter

Taste Salt; caramel; whipped cream; banana; nut; clay; minerals; candied lemon rind.

Latte

Leone ✿ ✿

Latte has a tasteful slightly stone-ground texture that evokes past traditions and values. This scrumptious bar carries so many flavours that it is hard to believe that ingredients such as coffee or nuts are not used. The unrefined sugar, lush milk, cream and Mexican vanilla expand the cocoa's richness, giving it a complex sweetness without excess. **Leone say** The goodness of these bars lies in a secret: the exclusive use of fresh milk from the Piedmont region, which together with the finest Asiatic cacao gives the chocolate the natural taste of childhood memories. Guido Monero (left) has succeeded in finding a technique to work with fresh milk, guaranteeing the consumer an extraordinary taste experience. **Cacao** Origins include Samoa, Ceylon and Java. **Established** In 1857 in Alba, Piedmont, by Luigi Leone (top left) who made sweets in his small confectionary shop. In 1880 Luigi moved his thriving company to old stables in a courtyard on Corso Vittorio Emanuele II, Turin. In 1934, after his death, the Monero family, experienced in confectionary, bought Leone. They made 242 Corso Regina Margerita (a former safe factory) the new workshop. The Leone sign is still on its art deco exterior. The company is now located in the Collegno district. **Made** In Turin.

Milk chocolate Blended with vanilla.

●●●Milk ●●Sweet ●●Cocoa 44% ●●Vanilla ●●Butter

Taste Coffee; coconut; hazelnut; chestnut; almond; clear honey; whole milk; vanilla fudge; cream; nutmeg; black pepper. Hint of peanut butter.

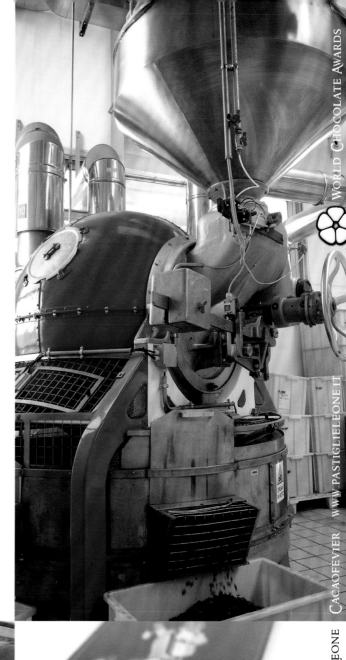

WWW.PASTIGLIELEONE.IT

LEONE CACAOFEVIER

Cioccolato Latte con Pistacchi di Sicilia Interi

Leone ✿ ✿ ✿

Leone's luscious full-milk, full-flavour chocolate with the addition of exquisite delicate pistachios. The green gems are consistently distributed in a tasteful quantity and have a tender texture. Their perfect flavour is complimented by the chocolate to create a gastronomic treat. **Leone say** The Sicilian pistachio is embraced in the cocoa aroma and becomes a delicacy. Tasty and nutty pieces for a rich and out-of-the-ordinary chocolate. **Cacao** Origins include Samoa, Ceylon and Java. **Pictured** On arrival, cacao beans are inspected, cleaned of debris, and loaded into a funnel (above). Beneath it is a powerful fan that propels them up the metal pipe and into the funnel above the ball roaster, visible in the background. Guido Monero had many of his vintage machines painted in the Italian tricolore, including the roaster. Right: cocoa paste is fed through a safety grille onto either three or five metal rollers to refine it.

Milk chocolate Blended with vanilla. Containing whole pistachios.

●●Milk   ●●Sweet   ●●Cocoa 44%   ●●Butter   ●Pistachio   ●Vanilla

Taste Toast; lightly roasted pistachio; coffee; coconut; hazelnut; chestnut; almond; clear honey; whole milk; vanilla fudge; cream; nutmeg; black pepper. Hint of peanut butter.

Leone Cacaofèvier www.pastiglieleone.it

CIOCCOLATO CON NOCCIOLE PIEMONTE INTERE

Leone ✦

The inclusion of petite hazelnuts adds a delicate accompaniment and a satisfying munch to Leone's sensational chocolate, which is the centrepiece. **Leone say** The Tonda Gentile hazelnut from the Langhe area of Piedmont is brought together with the milk chocolate for an unmistakable taste, recalling the city of Turin. Tasty and unexpected nutty pieces for a rich and out of the ordinary chocolate. **Cacao** Origins include Samoa, Ceylon and Java. **Interestingly** It is extraordinary to see fresh milk and cream listed in the ingredients of a chocolate: instead of using dry powdered milk, Guido Monero studied antique books regarding the manufacture of chocolate by the "wet" method to give Leone its special dairy flavours. Every morning fresh milk from the dairies in the mountains surrounding Turin is delivered to Leone and processed in-house into a paste from which the moisture is removed. The result is that it becomes solid, fairly hard and porous, with a crystallised texture (pictured centre left and right). It can be then ground into a powder to add to the chocolate on the same day. Below: the flat conche, which slowly grinds the chocolate between its granite roller and base. The yellow pillars in the background have motion detectors to halt the conche for safety if anyone approaches.

Milk chocolate Blended with vanilla. Containing small whole hazelnuts.

●●Milk   ●●Sweet   ●●Cocoa 44%   ●●Butter   ●Hazelnut   ●Vanilla

Taste Toast; lightly roasted hazelnut; coffee; coconut; chestnut; almond; clear honey; whole milk; vanilla fudge; cream; nutmeg; black pepper. Hint of peanut butter.

CACAOFÉVIER — WWW.PASTIGLIELEONE.IT

LEONE

275

Cioccolato al Latte

Rivoire ⊗ ⊗

This buttery blend coaxes smooth and graceful flavours from the hazelnut and earthy cacao. A pinch of salt enhances the harmonious recipe. **Cacao** A blend of several origins. **Established** In 1872 in Florence's Piazza della Signoria (below) by Enrico Rivoire of Turin, chocolatier to the Savoy Royal family. The salon and workshop which introduced the city to the Savoy drinking chocolate stand opposite the splendid Palazzo Vecchio (Old Palace, right) the seat of power during the years when Florence was Italy's capital. In 1977 the Rivoire family business passed into the hands of the Bardelli brothers, who continue Rivoire's traditions, including the toasting cacao beans in-house. **Made** In Florence, Tuscany.

Milk chocolate Blended with hazelnut paste and salt.

●●●Butter ●●●Sweet ●●Hazelnut ●●Milk ●Cocoa 32% ●Salt

Taste Roast hazelnut; butter; honey; chocolate; salt; cream. Hint of caramel, black pepper and cinnamon.

Nocciolato al Latte

Rivoire ✿ ✿

The trio of tangy flavours are instantly recognisable and unforgettable: a magnificent roasted hazelnut taste enhanced by salt and the nuances of a soft, but meaningful, cocoa blend. **Rivoire say** Artisan chocolatiers since, 1872, we continue to use traditional production methods. Each process is carried out exactly. From the selection of raw materials to the mixing of products, creation of chocolate and choice of elegant boxes, everything is still done by hand. **Cacao** A blend of several origins. **Interestingly** It was Florentine Francesco Carletti who first brought knowledge of cacao and chocolate to Italy. His book, Chronicles of My Voyage Around the World (Ragionamenti del Mio Viaggio Intorno al Mondo) written in July 1606 recounted his experiences for Fernando de' Medici, Grand Prince of Tuscany.

Milk chocolate Blended with hazelnut paste. Scattered on one side with whole hazelnuts.

●●●Butter   ●●●Hazelnut   ●●Cocoa 32%   ●●Sweet
●●Milk   ●●Salt

Taste Roast hazelnut; double cream; butter; salt; molasses; malt; biscuit. Hint of caramel; coffee and cinnamon.

CREMA NOCCIOLA AL CACAO
Rivoire ⊗

Grand roasted hazelnut flavours that are beautifully rounded, underscored by caramel, butter and a range of indulgently rich chocolate notes. **Rivoire say** A high percentage of cocoa and ancient jealously guarded recipes help to create all the delicacies that have made Rivoire world renown. **Interestingly** Crema nocciola, also called Gianduja (pronounced jan-do-yah) is a tender Italian speciality made of chocolate and hazelnut paste, which is ground so fine and smooth that the Italians say "hazelnut cream." Combined into a soft paste, it is pressed into a traditional bite-sized trapezoid shape and wrapped (see page 279). Alternatively it can be packaged in a jar for use as a spread, in which case different pastes may be produced in a range of fluidity between soft paste and semi liquid (which Rivoire's Crema nocciola is).

Milk chocolate paste Blended with hazelnut paste.

●●●Hazelnut ●●Butter ●●Cocoa ●●Sweet ●●Milk ●Oil

Taste Roast hazelnut; roast Brazil nut; sesame; honey; whole milk; toffee; molasses; malt. Hint of vanilla and salt.

€1,70 l'etto
miscela *Beethoven*
€ 17.00 al Kg.
4

€1,60 l'etto
miscela *Napoleone*
€ 16.00 al Kg.
5

It's a great partnership between two deeply aromatic and charismatic ingredients: crisp dark coffee nibs and medium-dark chocolate. Splendid roasted flavours on both accounts are complimented with rich, fresh, creamy milk. **Slitti say** Caffè al Latte is a chocolate which combines a prestigious selection of cocoa with top quality aromatic coffee. Gran Bouquet was created to enhance the basic taste of chocolate combined with the aromas of distant lands. **Cacao** A blend of several origins. **Established** In 1969 by Luciano Slitti (below) as a coffee roasting workshop. In 1988 he and his sons Andrea and Daniele brought their expertise to the roasting of cacao beans and created their own range of chocolates. **Made** In Monsummano Terme, Tuscany.

Milk chocolate Blended with vanilla. Containing small coffee bean nibs.

●●●Coffee ●●Cocoa 45% ●●Sweet ●●Milk ●●Butter ●●Vanilla ●Bitter

Taste Coffee; roast; cream; rich continental hot chocolate; caramel. Hint of fruit and berry.

GRAN BOUQUET CAFFÈ LATTE
Slitti ⊗ ⊗

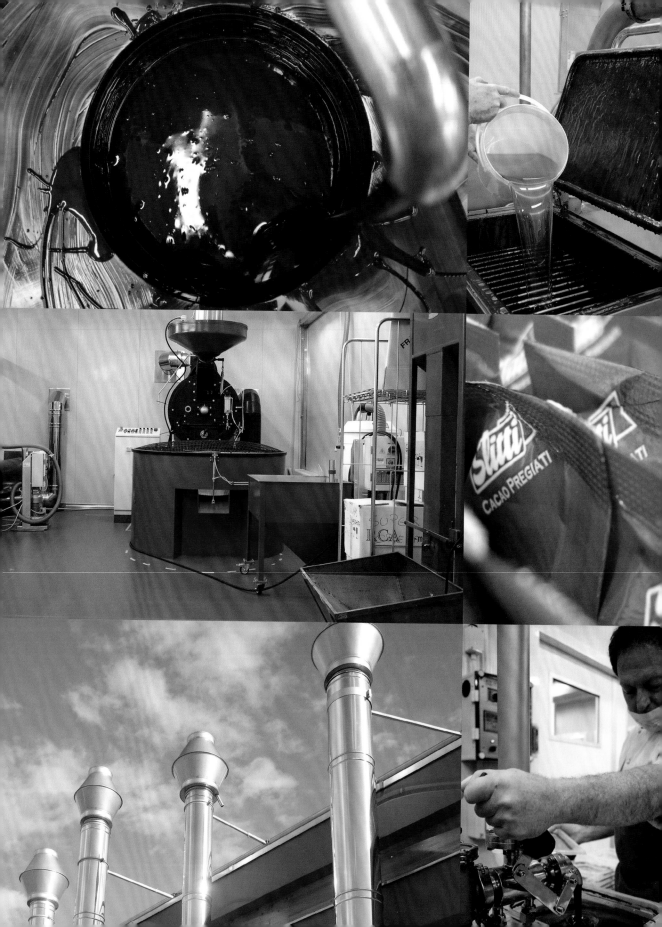

LatteNero 45%
Slitti ✿

LatteNero certainly lives up to its name, meaning DarkMilk: rich roasted cocoa tones - similar to those of a continental hot chocolate - are complimented by thick cream. Robust and satisfying with a long-lasting finish. **Slitti say** LatteNero is a top quality milk chocolate. Its particular taste is given by the high percentage of cocoa, which is selected at the origin from the most prestigious plantations. LatteNero is unique, as characterised by perfect balance between cocoa, milk and sugar. Thus being able to satisfy even the most demanding gourmets. **Cacao** A blend of several origins. **Interestingly** Just a cacao bean's throw away from the shop, which is an Aladdin's cave of coffee and chocolate creations, stands the new Slitti chocolate factory. Completed in 2012 to Andrea Slitti's specification and finished in the family's trademark colours. Even the texture of the walls is identical to that of the chocolate boxes. Upper left: Andrea adds melted cocoa butter to the chocolate in the conche. Lower and centre left: the roaster and its chimney.

Milk chocolate Blended with vanilla.

●●Cocoa 45% ●●Sweet ●●Milk ●●Butter
●●Vanilla ●Bitter

Taste Continental hot chocolate; vanilla fudge; chocolate mousse; cream; caramel; hazelnut; roast. Hint of dried fig, ripe banana and lemon zest.

LatteNero 51%

Slitti ✦

It's easy to imagine that you are savouring tender creamy coconut with a smooth dark chocolate as LatteNero 51% slowly melts in your mouth. The decadent qualities of both cream and roasted cacao are brought together harmoniously and with great refinement. **Slitti say** The balanced flavour obtained by LatteNero is amazing. The relationship between milk, sugar and cocoa gives an aromatic and full taste. This creates fantastic combinations that dark chocolate alone can not permit. One of the main secrets of LatteNero is the selection of cocoa types: they should not cover the delicate milk flavour, they should confer more aroma. **Cacao** A blend of several origins. **Pictured** 51% is also available in boxes of Mattonelle (squares, above). Left: Slitti's rich thick hot chocolate (cioccolata) is served in the store's seated area, where there is a library of chocolate recipe and history books to browse.

Milk chocolate Blended with vanilla.

●●●Cocoa 51%   ●●Milk   ●●Sweet   ●●Butter   ●Vanilla   ●Bitter

Taste Coconut cream; caramel; wood; deep roast; double cream; treacle; chocolate mousse. Hint of tahini, cinnamon, celery and black pepper.

SLITTI CACAOFÉVIER WWW.SLITTI.IT

287

LatteNero 62%
Slitti ✿ ✿

Intense, aromatic roasted cacao, balanced and rounded by lavish and fresh creamy notes. 62 will appeal to those with a taste for exploring deep cacao flavours and luxurious dairy notes: vanilla and sugar are used very carefully. **Slitti say** LatteNero is a top quality milk chocolate. Its particular taste is given by the high percentage of cocoa which is selected at the origin from the most prestigious plantations. **Cacao** A blend of several origins. **Interestingly** A story in pictures: whilst brushing it, the chocolate is kept warm by an infra-red lamp. Next, the coated slab is sliced into squares by the wires of a guitar cutter, ready to be placed on a conveyor belt. Each square passes through a curtain of chocolate, and then under the hands of a lady who gently places a plastic mould on top of it, using her fingertips or a sponge to apply slight pressure. The pieces proceed through a tunnel of cool air and through the wall into a room where the mould is carefully removed and the chocolates are packed by hand in boxes.

Milk chocolate Blended with vanilla.

●●●Cocoa ●●Butter ●●Milk ●Bitter ●Sweet

Taste Deep roast; mushroom; dark chocolate gateaux, double cream; charred wood; tobacco; red wine; lemon pith. Hint of nut, blueberry and cranberry.

LATTENERO 70%

Slitti ⚘⚘

The robust deep-roasted cacao is rounded off with a good portion of thick fresh cream. It's rich enough to match the classic dark chocolate flavours: this is a powerful duet. Vanilla and sugar have been used very conservatively in this extra dark milk chocolate. **Slitti say** LatteNero is unique, as characterised by perfect balance between cocoa, milk and sugar. Thus being able to satisfy even the most demanding gourmets. **Cacao** A blend of several origins. **Pictured** Above: Easter eggs, during production. They are decorated using techniques such as melting a hole with a hairdryer or drizzling chocolate from a height. Opposite: the incomparable detail of Slitti's Ferri Vecchi (Rusted Tools) made of 60% dark chocolate and dusted with cocoa powder.

Milk chocolate Blended with vanilla.

●●●Cocoa 70% ●●Milk ●●Butter ●●Bitter ●Sweet ●●Bitter

Taste Cream; deep roast; mushroom; charred wood; tobacco; lemon pith; coconut cream. Hint of nut, smoke, vanilla, honey, cinnamon and dark cherry.

BIANCO UVETTA

Vestri ✿ ✿

Vestri's ivory-tinted chocolate bends and tears rather than snaps, because it is blended with a good portion of hazelnut paste. The extroverted sweetness, mellowed by the gentle nutty qualities, is well matched to the taste of the tender sultanas. To understand how it tastes, imagine that you are enjoying all of the above with a rich vanilla gelato... **Established** In 1960 by Daniele Vestri. **Made** In the workshop and store in Arezzo, Tuscany. **Interestingly** There is also a caffé and pasticceria (pastry shop) on site. Vestri roast their own coffee beans, offering a selection of single origins to try. But do not forget their hot chocolate and gelati, which are possible to combine in a cup "affogato" (drowned).

Non-deodorised white chocolate Blended with vanilla and hazelnut paste. Containing sultanas.

●●●Sweet   ●●●Butter   ●●Milk   ●●Vanilla   ●●Sultana   ●Hazelnut

Taste Sultana; vanilla gelato; honey; caramel; malt; potato; butter; hazelnut. Hint of salt.

BIANCO PISTACCHI

Vestri ⊗

Exceedingly sweet, nutty and tasty, thanks to Vestri's recipe for white chocolate that includes hazelnut paste and a flavoursome cocoa butter. **Interestingly** Six years ago Vestri acquired an eight hectare cacao plantation, Hacienda Vista Alegre, in Punta Cana, Dominican Republic. This makes them one of very few chocolatiers in the world to grow their own cacao. Furthermore, it is cultivated to organic standards. **Pictured** Vestri have opened a second shop in Tuscany, situated in Florence.

Non-deodorised white chocolate Blended with vanilla and hazelnut paste. Containing whole pistachios.

●●●Sweet ●●●Butter ●●●Vanilla ●●Milk
●●Pistachio ●Hazelnut

Taste Pistachio gelato; cashew; roast pistachio; potato; butter; malt; caramel; vanilla; hazelnut. Hint of salt.

I Sapori
Pistacchi

VESTRI

Cioccolato bianco
WHITE CHOCOLATE

50g ℮ Net wt 1.7 oz.

LITHUANIA

ORGANIC MILK

Naive ✷

Sometimes you can judge a chocolate by its wrapper: this bar has a charmingly unconventional character. Delightful details soon emerge from the principal flavours. This is a chocolate with plenty going on: intriguing winter spices, mouth-watering chalky sherbet fruit pastilles and muted fruit notes to savour. There's a hint of dryness and the wet creaminess of the milk. The slight texture is also extraordinary and quirky, with a popping candy quality to it as it melts. **Naive say** The sweet and creamy milk combined with the Naive cacao house-blend creates this smooth dark-milk combination. **Cacao** A blend of beans from Haiti and Uganda. **Made** In Giedraiciai, a small village 60km from Vilnius, capital of Lithuania. **Established** In 2010 by Domantas Uzpalis (pictured) who signs each bar's wrapper by hand. **Interestingly** Naive use a fluid bed roaster, in which heat is transferred to the cacao bean from only the air. In a conventional roaster the heat transfers from the sides of a hot metal drum.

Milk chocolate Blended with vanilla.

●●Sweet   ●●Cocoa 43%   ●●Butter   ●●Milk 18%   ●Vanilla   ●Sour

Taste Candied orange peel; Barratts Refreshers; lime; nut; whole milk; flower. Hint of cinnamon and ginger.

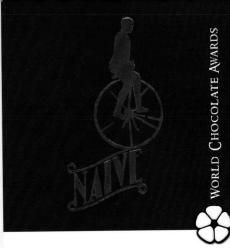

NAÏVE CACAOFÉVIER   WWW.CHOCOLATENAIVE.COM

MADAGASCAR

MILK CHOCOLATE
Madécasse ⊗ ⊗

A dark milk chocolate with a very interesting and engaging character. Its attributes include smoothness from creamy milk, fudge, and fine texture, balanced by the richness of deep roasted cacao. Sweetness is joined by salt, hints of berry acidity and traces of cocoa bitterness. **Madécasse say** A "dark" milk bar with clear notes of caramel. **Cacao** Criollo and trinitario from the Ezaka Cooperative, Anjiabory, north west Madagascar. **Established** In 2006. The chocolate and vanilla company, based in Brooklyn, New York, was founded by Brett Beach (a former embassy employee and seaweed farmer) and Tim McCollum (former American Express brand manager in Manhattan) who were Peace Corps volunteers in Madagascar. **Interestingly** Madécasse is one of only a handful of chocolate bars in the world that are made in the same country that the cacao is grown in. They believe that this creates four times the impact of fairly traded cacao. **Made** In the Cinagra factory, Antananarivo, Madagascar for Madécasse. Here every stage from cleaning and roasting the beans to wrapping the chocolate bar by hand takes place.

Milk chocolate Blended with vanilla.

●●Cocoa 44%   ●●Sweet   ●●Milk   ●●Butter   ●Vanilla   ●Salt   ●Sour   ●Bitter

Taste Creamy fudge; salted caramel; malt; molasses; dark chocolate cake; biscuit; Brazil nut; tobacco; orange peel; red berry; wholemeal toast. Hint of honey.

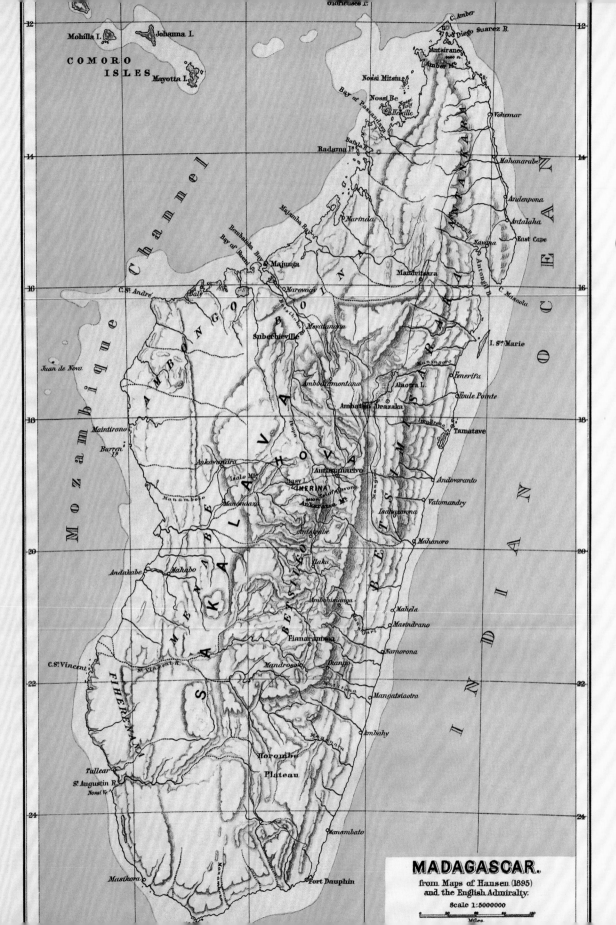

WORLD CHOCOLATE AWARDS

MADAGASCAR.

from Maps of Hausen (1895)
and the English Admiralty.

Scale 1:5000000

Miles.

303

MILK CHOCOLATE
Menakao ✿ ✿

It's easy to imagine salted butter-caramel popcorn, as you savour these long notes. This sweet and salty chocolate develops an impressive creamy vanilla fudge taste too. These unique, charismatic, flavours are bold and balanced. **Menakao say** An original yet elegant milk chocolate, whose buttery and vanilla notes are reminiscent of the indulgence of fudge, and which delicately transition to a light atmosphere. All this is conveyed by the fruity and citrus aromas which are characteristic of the Madagascan cacao beans. **Cacao** From organic plantations in the Sambirano Valley, north west Madagascar. **Established** Menakao was founded in 2010. **Made** For Menakao in the Cinagra factory (pictured, with it's owner Cassam Chenai, above) situated 15km from Antananarivo, Madagascar's capital. **Interestingly** "Mena" means red in Malagasy, a reference to the cacao beans and soil of the "Red Island."

Milk chocolate Blended with vanilla.

●●●Butter ●●Sweet ●●Salt ●●Cocoa 44% ●●Milk ●●Vanilla

Taste Salted butter caramel; popcorn; vanilla chocolate fudge; Brazil nut. Hint of pineapple, banana, smoke, spice, malt.

PERU

COCONUT

Orquidea ✿ ✿

This milky chocolate has fine, light notes that come purely from the cocoa: no vanilla is used. Its sweetness is soothed by the oils and flavours of hundreds of chewy, but tender, pieces of coconut. The delicious ingredients are well matched: this is an exquisite example of coconut with milk chocolate. **Orquidea say** Shredded and lightly toasted coconut is mixed with our velvety smooth milk chocolate. Our coconuts are locally sourced, providing the freshest shaved coconut available. Orquidea chocolates are handmade with pure cacao in the San Martin valleys in the jungles of the Peruvian Amazon. **Cacao** Criollo and forastero from San Martin, Peru. **Made** In Tarapoto, San Martin, Peru. **Established** 1998 in Tarapoto. A small plant was built to craft cacao beans into chocolate bars, with training provided by Swiss technicians. By sourcing cacao from local farmers and training them in its cultivation, it helped to make growing cacao a viable alternative to coca bushes.

Milk chocolate Containing small pieces of coconut.

●●Sweet ●●Coconut ●●Milk ●●Butter ●Cocoa 35%

Taste Coconut; flower; honey; whole milk; caramel.

SPAIN

PIZZA REGINA MARGHERITA

Enric Rovira ✿

Vivid sun dried tomato and basil flavours develop and delight as the sweet and salty chocolate melts away. The experience culminates in a big finish of classic savoury Italian flavours. A unique experience that is bound to appeal to those who appreciate the combination of salt and sugar in recipes. **Enric Rovira says** A chocolate inspired by the Margherita pizza created in Naples in honour of the Queen of Italy and made with three ingredients: mozzarella, tomato and basil, the colours of the Italian flag. In our version we substitute the original cheese with white chocolate. **Established** In spring 2003 by Enric and his second cousin Francesc Forrellat. Until then, Enric had worked in his parents' pastry shop, the well-known Pastisseria Rovira on Carrer de Gelabert in Barcelona. The philosophy of the new enterprise was to create high quality chocolate products with contemporary designs, linked to the city of Barcelona, Enric's hometown. **Made** In Castellbell i el Vilar, 60km North West of Barcelona.

White chocolate Blended with vanilla and salt. Containing crumbs of dried basil and tomato.

●●●Sweet   ●●●Salt   ●●●Butter
●●Milk   ●●Basil   ●●Tomato

Taste Sun dried tomato; dry basil; oregano; salty pizza dough.

ENRIC ROVIRA

PIZZA

Regina Margherita

cioccolato bianco con pomodoro e basilico
chocolate blanco con tomate y albahaca
white chocolate with tomato and basil

80 g - 2.82 oz

ENRIC ROVIRA   WWW.ENRICROVIRA.COM

Amaretti

Enric Rovira ✴

Crunchy pieces of amaretti give a sophisticated flavour (and texture) to the sweet caramel and deep, slightly dark, chocolaty notes of the bar. A great combination, with each part enhancing the other. **Enric Rovira says** The most bitter milk chocolate with a crisp texture. More than just a chocolate bar. Chocolate with ingredients that lend it freshness, uniqueness and texture, bringing out the flavour of the cocoa. Basic blends presented in the form of a square bar with an exclusive design, making it easier to eat. No doubt, these bars are the first in the world to allow you to break off single pieces at a time. **Pictured** Spanish architect Josep Puig i Cadafalch designed many significant places in Barcelona at the turn of the last century, including the Casa Terrades, Casaramona Factory and Plaça Espanya, as well as the rajoles street paving (left) from which one range of Enric Rovira's chocolate bars take its name and form. Below: Antoni Gaudí's beautiful hexagonal paving design, inspired by the sea, used in the Passeig de Gràcia, is also recreated in chocolate form. Right: a tribute to Barcelona Zoo's very rare albino gorilla, Snowflake.

Milk chocolate Blended with vanilla. Containing minute pieces of amaretti.

●●●Sweet　●●Butter　●●Milk　●●Amaretti　●●Vanilla　●●Cocoa 40%

Taste Caramel; vanilla fudge; roast; classic chocolate; milk; wheat biscuit; apricot kernel; nut. Hint of coffee, cinnamon and malt.

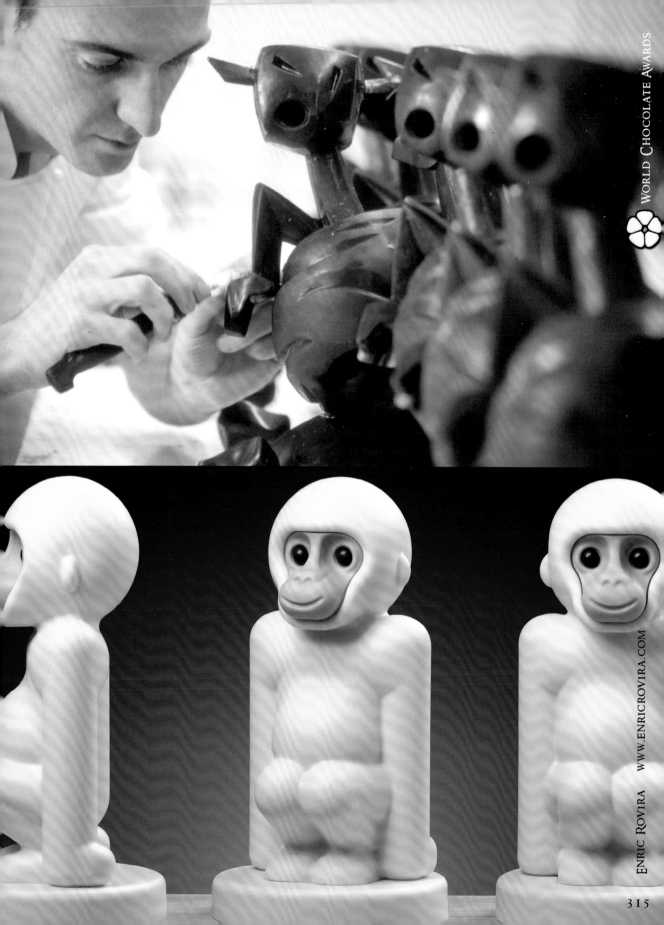

ENRIC ROVIRA WWW.ENRICROVIRA.COM

SWITZERLAND

BLANC NOUGATINE AMANDE
Alter Eco Europe ⊗

Something out of the ordinary: suave cream, enriched with vanilla, carrying tender almond nibs and brittle caramel to munch. This sweet indulgent treat is also distinguished by its great grain flavours. **Alter Eco say** A chocolate like no other! A delectable white chocolate with generous bursts of crunchy almond nougat. Smooth and organic, made without emulsifier, it is the key to a world of great taste and pleasure. **Cacao butter** From the Conacado co-operative in Dominican Republic, which brings together more than eight thousand small producers, from over one hundred village associations across the country. **Made** In Switzerland. **Established** In 1998 by Tristan Lecomte in France, Alter Eco is a company that specialises in unique food products. "Everything we buy is Fairtrade, organic and carbon neutral." Says Tristan. In 2005, Alter Eco expanded into the United States, headed by Mathieu Senard and Edouard Rollet in San Francisco. In 2006 Alter Eco Australia was founded in Sydney by Ilse Keijzer. **Pictured** Cacao is normally fermented for three to eight days to improve its flavour. The time depends mostly on the variety, quantity, the weather, and the temperature of the environment. Criollo require less time than forastero. Trinitario vary between the two. The wet beans are piled in wood fermentation boxes on the same day that they are separated from the pods and the placenta that connects them. The boxes do not have lids, the pile is covered with banana leafs or jute sacks to conserve heat and moisture. Fermentation happens in two stages: first anaerobic (without air) then aerobic (requiring air). During the first stage heat is generated as the sugars in the sweet whitish pulp that covers the beans are converted into alcohol by naturally occurring yeast and bacteria. Holes in the boxes allow pulp to drain out as it turns dark and liquefies, optimising conditions for the second stage. Conversions that change flavour also take place inside the bean at this time. Aerobic fermentation begins after a day or two, when all the sugars have been converted to alcohol. Naturally occurring bacteria then convert the alcohol to vinegar. This gives the pile a strong rich smell, similar to that of balsamic vinegar and red wine. Important reactions continue inside the bean, which absorbs some of the vinegar. The temperature of the pile soars and care is taken to restrict it to around 45-50°C and ensure an even fermentation, by turning the pile of beans over with a wooden shovel. Fermentation also kills the beans (which are seeds) preventing them from germinating and spoiling. Fermentation is monitored by cutting beans open lengthwise and evaluating their interior colour and texture. Greyish beans are not fermented. Pictured near right: violet (or white in pale varieties) indicates insufficient fermentation. Far right: defined grooves and a liver colour (or cinnamon in pale varieties) indicate fermented beans. When the majority of beans are satisfactory, the fermentation is halted by the beans being laid out to dry.

White chocolate Blended with vanilla. Containing minute almond nibs and caramel brittle.

●●●Sweet   ●●●Vanilla   ●●Butter 30%   ●●Almond   ●●Caramel   ●●Milk

Taste White bread toast; caramel; malt; corn; wheat; salt; egg nog; vanilla; roasted almond. Hint of golden syrup.

ORGANICO

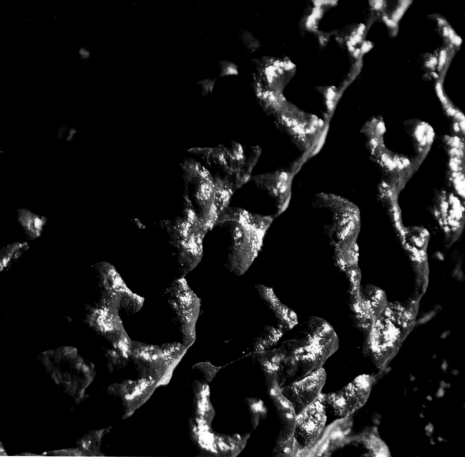

DARK VELVET

NOIR DOUX & FONDANT

Alter Eco Europe & Americas ⊗ (

An impressively deep, rich, satisfying, dark chocolate with cream, which reveals delightful hints of blackcurrants. More interesting details follow, enriching the waves of midnight chocolate. **Alter Eco say** Stronger than a milk chocolate, and more tender melting than a classic dark chocolate. Grown in the heart of the Peruvian Amazon, our cocoa is distinguished by powerful and fruity aromas that give our chocolates a character unique and very different from a conventional chocolate bar. **Cacao** From the Acopagro co-operative (pictured with Alter Eco's Tristan Lecomte) in the San Martín region of the Peruvian Amazon. **Interestingly** Acopagro was established by twenty seven cacao farmers in 1997 as part of a United Nations project to eradicate coca cultivation and its associated problems in what was at the time a conflict-torn region in crisis. The co-operative has steadily grown to near two thousand farmers who produce about four thousand metric tons of cacao beans annually. Quality standards are high for their export grade beans: 85-90% fermentation. Fermentation grades affect price because it is a key stage in the development of flavour, highly valued by cacaofèviers. However the grade of the beans used in chocolates is rarely disclosed to the consumer.

Milk chocolate.

●●●Cocoa 47%   ●●Sweet   ●Butter   ●Milk   ●Sour   ●Bitter

Taste Treacle toffee; dark chocolate cake; cream; tobacco; prune; fig; grape; blackcurrant; grapefruit; lemon zest; honeydew melon; star anise; ripe banana; anise. Hint of coffee and herbs.

ACOPAGRO
COOPERATIVA AGRARIA CACAOTERA

"CACAO CON SABOR
A CHOCOLATE"

World Chocolate Awards

© ALTER ECO — WWW.ALTERECO-USA.COM · WWW.ALTERECO-USA.COM

HIMBEER

Maestrani ✹

Zesty fresh lemon and raspberry give Himbeer a considerable acidic fruity bite, countering the sweet chocolate. The creamy white chocolate is of the highest quality. Altogether a lively, stimulating and invigorating experience. **Maestrani say** White Swiss chocolate with raspberries. The light, fruity chocolate for all those who love fruit: trendy, fresh and with an unmistakable fruity sweet-sour flavour. **Established** In 1852 in Lucerne. The Maestrani family were connected with cocoa since 1829, when Giuseppe Maestrani produced and sold chocolate in the old Via Nassa near the shore of lake Lugano in Switzerland. Like many inhabitants of Val Blenio, he had learnt how to manufacture chocolate in nearby Lombardy, Italy. His son, Aquilino, was of great help to his father since childhood, and after several years of learning and travelling, became his successor, founding Maestrani. Nowadays the company is owned by three different families and still works from the cacao beans, roasting and refining them in-house. **Made** In Flawil, North East Switzerland.

White chocolate Blended with vanilla. With powdered lemon and mixed with small pieces of freeze-dried raspberry.

●●●Rasberry ●●Lemon ●●Sweet ●●Butter 30% ●●Milk ●●Sour ●Vanilla

Taste Lemon juice; raspberry; honey; vanilla milkshake; light caramel.

MAESTRANI CACAOFÉVIER WWW.MAESTRANI.CH

323

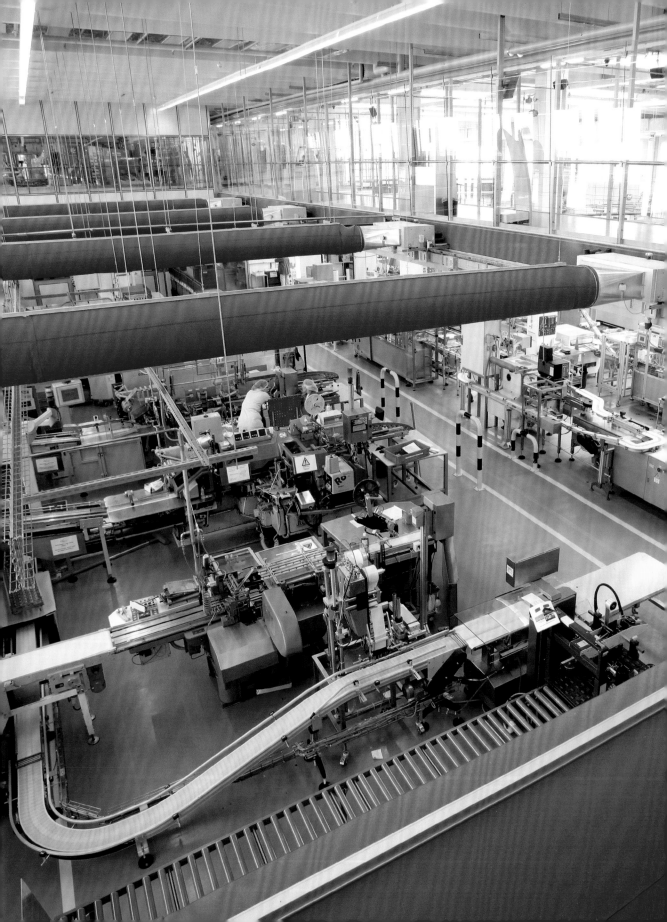

ERDBEER

Maestrani ✿

Strawberry has been paired with its soul mates in order to make a delicious, sophisticated, pink chocolate. Creamy and sweet, with a little drop of citrus and pinch of pepper to enhance the flavours. **Maestrani say** We have combined in this creation Swiss organic white chocolate with strawberries and black pepper. The result is a fruity, peppery and fresh touch with distinctive aromatic sweet sharpness. This recipe is ideal for all who love fruit in chocolate. Maestrani stands for exquisite taste. **Interestingly** Strawberry and raspberry plants are members of the rose family.

White chocolate Blended with vanilla and lemon oil. Containing small pieces of freeze-dried strawberry and crushed pepper.

●●●Strawberry   ●●●Lemon   ●●●Sweet   ●●Butter 33%   ●●Milk
●Vanilla   ●Black pepper   ●Sour

Taste Strawberry; lemon juice with zest; vanilla milkshake; honey; light caramel. Hint of black pepper.

325

DOPPEL MILCH

Maestrani ☯

Heavenly, creamy, sweet chocolate. With soul.
Maestrani say Finest Swiss milk chocolate.
With an extra portion of milk for lovers of
milk chocolates - milky, creamy, soft-melting,
with a slight taste of caramel. Premium brand
Maestrani chocolate bars are organic and
Fairtrade certified - sustainably excellent.
Interestingly Nearly one third of this
chocolate is milk, hence the name "Double
Milk." **Pictured** The factory (also known as
SchoggiLand) offers guided tours to the
public. Groups are able to book chocolate
moulding classes. There is also a factory
shop. Maestrani employs around one
hundred and eighty people and produces
3500 tons of chocolate products annually.
Maestrani's brands are sold in over thirty
countries.

Milk chocolate Blended with vanilla.

●●●Sweet   ●●●Milk   ●●Cocoa 37%
●Vanilla

Taste Toffee; honey; fromage frais; ripe
banana; chocolate mousse; whole milk;
hazelnut; malt. Hint of spice.

UNITED STATES OF AMERICA

Abundant and distinctive sweet fruit, nut and spice flavours make this harmonious composition one of the must-tastes of fine milk chocolate. As it melts away new intriguing and tasteful flavours evolve, perhaps reminiscent of the children's confections that change flavour. **Amano say** This chocolate is truly unlike any other milk chocolate you have ever tried. We use only the highest quality whole milk, and it is blended with one of the world's greatest cacao beans, which come exclusively from the Ocumare Valley. Just as the beans produce an absolutely incredible dark chocolate, they produce a milk chocolate that is equally as rich, complex, and utterly beautiful. **Cacao** Criollo from Ocumare, Venezuela. **Established** In 2006 by Art Pollard and Clark Goble, who had worked together in a university physics department, and then joined forces to create a successful software company. Amano Chocolate took ten years to evolve from simple idea to finished product. Lamenting the poor quality of chocolate in America, Art (right) applied his scientific background and curious nature to the study of chocolate. In his garage he tinkered with traditional chocolate-making equipment, refining the manufacturing process until it produced the desired result. He also built relationships with farmers on his many field trips. **Made** In Orem, Utah. **Interestingly** Amano means "by hand" in Italian, which represents their dedication to creating the finest chocolate, taking the necessary time with each batch to ensure that it is just right. Amano also means "they love" in Italian, hinting at Amano's love for fine chocolate. In Japanese, the word means "heavenly field," which connects with cacao being known as the "food of the gods."

Milk chocolate Blended with vanilla.

●●●Cocoa 30% ●●Sweet ●●Milk ●●Butter ●Vanilla

Taste Liquorice; cinnamon; melon; honey; plum; blueberry; almond; hazelnut; milk. Hint of red apple.

OCUMARE
Amano ✿ ✿ ✿

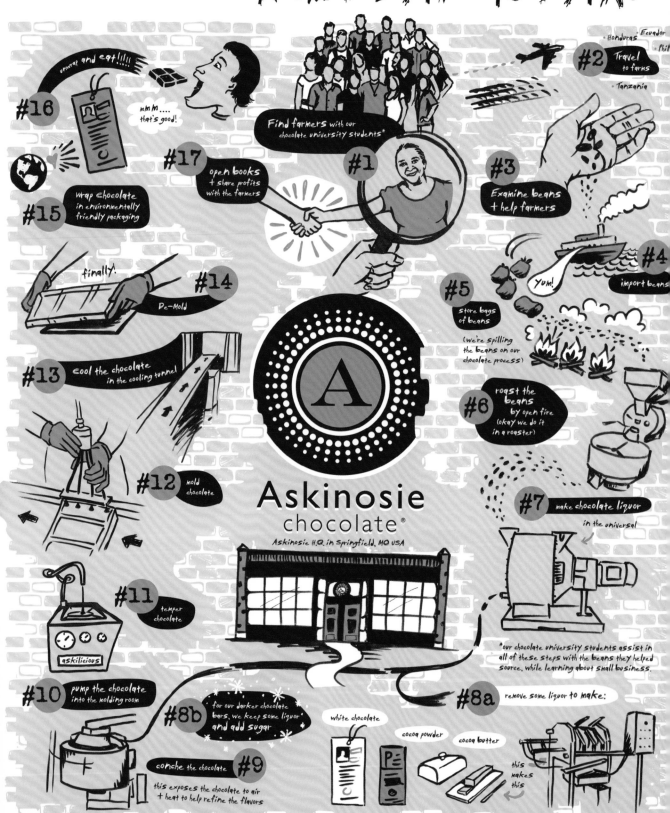

WHITE CHOCOLATE

Askinosie ✿

Three unique tastes await you inside this intriguing sweet bar: flavoursome cane juice dominates; then fragrant light notes of goat milk and nutty, aromatic, cocoa butter. **Askinosie say** Cooling mouth feel, rich buttery sweetness reminiscent of confectioner's sugar and velvet icing. Simple, soft, delicate, delightful. The non-deodorised cocoa butter is pressed in our factory and we are the first American small-batch chocolate maker to do this. After pressing our beans to create the cocoa butter, we combine it with goat's milk powder and organic cane juice, then craft it for days in our eighty five year old German melanguer, making ours one of the only single origin white chocolates in the world. **Cacao** Trinitario from Davao, Philippines. **Established** In 2005 Shawn Askinosie made his first batch of chocolate in his kitchen, from beans that he had sourced online. "By the end of that summer I'd travelled to the Amazon to learn how cacao is harvested, where it comes from, how to influence flavour. Then I put together a business plan." After converting an old railway supply building, constructed in 1894, into a factory, the first commercial batch of Askinosie chocolate went on sale in May 2007. There are now thirteen people working full time at Askinosie. **Made** In Springfield, Missouri. **Pictured** Askinoise's chocolate process poster, designed by Kristina Sacci. The company is one of very few in the world to use cocoa butter that they have pressed from the beans themselves.

Non-deodorised white chocolate Made with goat milk.

●●●Sweet   ●●Butter 34%   ●●Milk

Taste Goat milk; peanut; cashew; honey; butter; sugar cane juice. Hint of icing sugar, lavender and water.

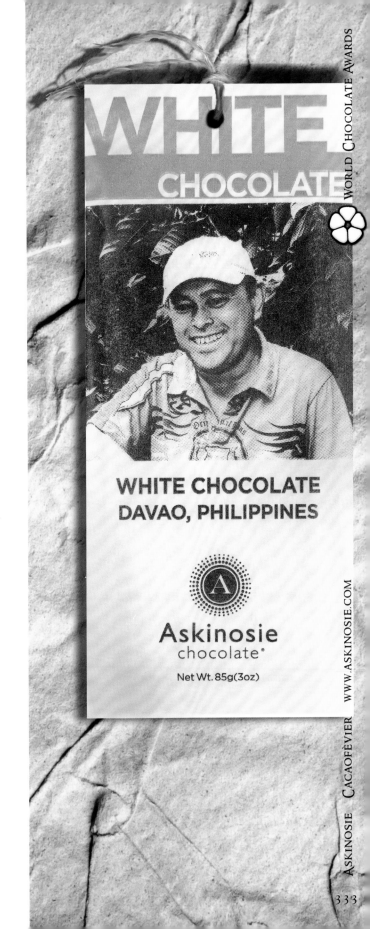

WHITE CHOCOLATE NIBBLE BAR
Askinosie ⊗

Enjoy the naturally nutty and tangy taste of cocoa butter, with hints of dark chocolate treats and the occasional bite provided by firm cocoa nibs. Subtle and sophisticated sweetness is contributed from the fusion of light, watery, aromatic goat milk and flavoursome tangy sugar cane. Goat milk permits a much cleaner, lighter taste profile, compared to the heavy and creamy characteristics of cow milk. **Askinosie say** Popping notes of browning sugar, honey, pear, cinnamon and zip. Buttery, cooling, crunchy meets creamy. **Cacao** The butter and nibs are from the same batch of trinitario beans from Davao, Mindanao island, Philippines (pictured).

Non-deodorised white chocolate Made with goat milk. Scattered on one side with cocoa nibs.

●●●Sweet ●●Butter 34% ●●Milk ●Cocoa ●Bitter

Taste Mild goat cheese; sugar cane juice; honey. Hint of nut, dark chocolate brownie, maple syrup and water.

cocoa nibs

igin: **Davao, Philippines**

joy by: **110414**

Askinosie
chocolate®

. Commercial St. · Springfield, MO
More information at ask

DARK MILK +FLEUR DE SEL

Askinosie ✽✽

A combination of sour and bitter, with sweet and savoury. This is a sensational dark recipe that will please those with an appetite for rich, slightly exotic, cocoa and treacle notes. The drop of goat milk is very accommodating to the cocoa flavours, with a cleaner, leaner flavour than cow's milk. **Askinosie say** Petal, almond, hints of vanilla, crème brulèe, caramel, mellow toasted oats with a salty finish. This is the first milk chocolate bar we have made in our factory. It is dark enough to satisfy your dark chocolate craving with a smooth and rich finish. To the cocoa liquor we add organic cane juice, goat's milk powder and a touch of fleur de sel sea salt. This bar is then crafted for hours in our Universal, a decades old machine made in Scotland. **Cacao** Trinitario from Davao, Mindanao island, the Philippines. **Interestingly** Shawn will not buy cacao unless he has been to meet the farmers first. This enables him to work with farmers, and teach them how to influence the taste of the beans to make the best chocolate. Although genotype, climate and soil influence flavour greatly, attention to harvesting ripe pods, even and thorough fermentation, precise drying, and good storage conditions are all important. Knowing the farmers also means traceability, and in addition to paying the farmers above Fair Trade prices for their cacao, Askinosie gives them ten percent of the net profits from the chocolate made with the beans from their crop. **Pictured** Kyle Malone, Shawn's son-in-law and Production Manager; Lawren Askinosie, Shawn's daughter and Director of Sales and Marketing; Shawn and Caron Askinosie. Top left: this mural was the outer wall of the neighbouring building. Exposed during the renovations for the first time in over one hundred years.

Goat milk chocolate. Blended with salt.

●●●Cocoa 62% ●Sweet ●Salt ●Goat Milk ●Butter ●Sour ●Bitter ●Dry

Taste Treacle toffee; lightly salted caramel; dark chocolate cake; charred wholemeal toast; butter; oat; lemon zest; liquorice. Hint of vanilla and roast nut.

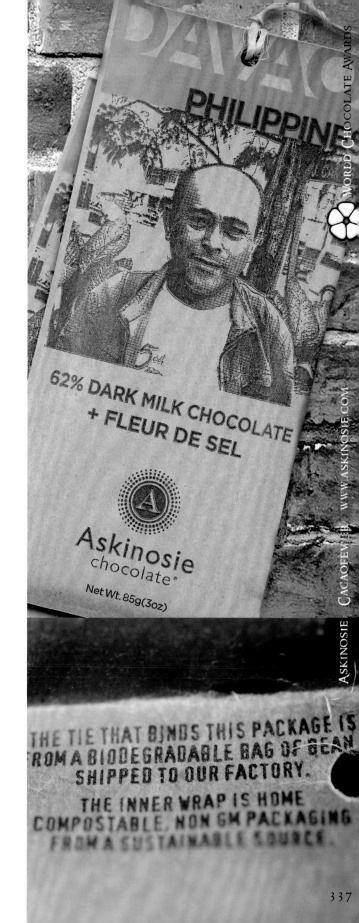

ASKINOSIE CACAOFEVER WWW.ASKINOSIE.COM

62% DARK MILK CHOCOLATE + FLEUR DE SEL

Askinosie chocolate®

Net Wt.85g(3oz)

THE TIE THAT BINDS THIS PACKAGE IS FROM A BIODEGRADABLE BAG OF BEAN SHIPPED TO OUR FACTORY.

THE INNER WRAP IS HOME COMPOSTABLE, NON GM PACKAGING FROM A SUSTAINABLE SOURCE.

White Chocolate+Pistachios

Askinosie ✳ ✳

The sweetness and richness of the cane juice is mellowed by refreshing light notes of goat milk, nutty cocoa butter, and tender pistachio. The intricacies of each are revealed in this tasty, tangy bar. **Askinosie say** Creamy white chocolate dancing with dry roasted, lightly salted, organic pistachio pieces. Crisp, buttery, wholesome, citrus. The main ingredient in our white chocolate is natural, non-deodorised cocoa butter. **Cacao** Trinitario from Davao, Mindanao island, Philippines (pictured). **Interestingly** The first cacao brought to Asia in 1600 was grown in the Philippines and Askinosie is the first cacaofèvier to import Filipino cacao beans in nearly twenty-five years. The Davao range is also the first single origin chocolate made with cacao from the Philippines.

Non-deodorised white chocolate Made with goat milk. Scattered on one side with lightly salted pistachios.

●●●Sweet ●●Butter 34% ●●Pistachio ●●Goat Milk ●Salt

Taste Goat milk; peanut; cashew; honey; butter; sugar cane juice; pistachio. Hint of icing sugar, lavender and water.

Dark Milk·Black Licorice
Askinosie ✲

An unforgettable balance of special flavours: full bodied, deep, and slightly dry chocolate with a long aftertaste; juicy, mouth-watering liquorice and anise. The latter add interesting textures to the tablet's crisp chocolate. **Askinosie say** We partnered with our friend (and Scandinavian distributor) Martin Jörgensen, and his liquorice factory, Lakritsfabriken, on this bar. We add organic cane juice, goat's milk powder, and a touch of fleur de sel sea salt. We then add bits of organic gluten-free salted black liquorice from Ramlösa, Sweden. This bar also includes anise seed, which enhances the liquorice flavour. **Cacao** Trinitario from Davao, Mindanao island, Philippines. **Interestingly** Lakritsfabriken launched in April 2011 with this single origin organic liquorice from Iran. It is free of gelatine and made with rice flour instead of wheat flour.

Goat milk chocolate Blended with sea salt. With anise seed and small pieces of salted black liquorice candy sprinkled on one side.

●●●Cocoa 62% ●●Liquorice ●Sweet ●Goat Milk ●Salt ●Bitter

Taste Molasses; malt; salt; anise; liquorice; deep roast; charred wood; coffee. Hint of milk and dark caramel.

DARK CHOCOLATE + MALTED MILK
Askinosie ⊛ ⊛

Seriously dark and flavoursome chocolate, with intriguing deep-roasted cocoa notes. It takes only a dash of refreshing, softening, malted milk to balance the dry hints and add another complex layer of flavour. A superb composition, with a fine texture. **Askinosie say** Floral notes met with strawberry, vanilla, and a barley malt sweetness. Creamy, velvety smooth. Each bite is like enjoying a chocolate malt at an old fashioned soda fountain. **Cacao** Trinitario from Tenende, situated in southwest Tanzania near Lake Malawi. **Interestingly** Askinosie's Chocolate University is a collaborative learning experience designed to inspire high school students about entrepreneurship, social business and a world beyond their own. Each year, a handful of students are selected to partake in this collaborative learning experience and travel with Shawn Askinosie to Tanzania. In its first year, they funded a deep water well to provide clean water to the two thousand villagers of Tenende.

Milk chocolate Blended with malted milk powder.

●●●Cocoa 60%   ●●Bitter   ●Sweet   ●Milk   ●Butter

Taste Deep roast; dark caramel; wholemeal toast; smoke; walnut; almond; hazelnut; malt. Hint of milk.

ASKINOSIE · CACAOFÉVIER · WWW.ASKINOSIE.COM

DARK
GOAT'S
MILK
Escazú ✿ ✿

Highly recommended because of its fortifying, tangy cocoa, rounded with moderate sweetness that may conjure dark cherry, tobacco and sweet spices. The creaminess of the goat milk develops subtly over time, allowing the taster to appreciate an evolution of the delicious dark and milk aspects of Escazú's flavoursome chocolate. **Escazú say** The chocolate makers' favourite. The mild tangy flavours of the goats milk blend well with earthy cacao. **Cacao** Carenero from Venezuela's central coastal region. **Established** In 2005 when Hallot (top right) Bob and Celia were on a trip to Costa Rica. A visit to a cacao plantation inspired them to make chocolate, and whilst staying in a town named Escazú, they began to make plans. In 2006 the first bars were made with in-house blends of Venezuelan chocolate and sold in a wine bar below the workshop. Soon other retail establishments became interested in the bars. The idea had become a serious business. In March 2008 Escazú's first bean-to-bar chocolate, Carenero 81%, went on sale, created by Hallot who had learnt through reading, trial and error. Since June 2009 all of Escazú's chocolates and confections (made by Venezuelan Danielle Centeno, lower right) have been made completely on-site. **Made** In the workshop and store in Raleigh, North Carolina. **Pictured** Above: after roasting, shelling and being cracked into nibs, cocoa is gently ground for several days by the rotating stones of a 1930's Spanish melangeur.

Goat milk chocolate Blended with vanilla.

●●●Cocoa 60%   ●●Sweet   ●●Butter ●●Vanilla   ●Goat Milk   ●Bitter

Taste Dark cherry; tobacco; roast; cinnamon; caramel; clove; mascarpone; dark chocolate gelato; barley; molasses; anise. Hint of almond and bay leaf.

Classic Milk Chocolate

Fruition Chocolate ⊗ ⊗

As promised by the name, this bar is full of great chocolaty, caramelised flavours... but there is much more to it. Vanilla plays an important role, yet the quantity and quality of the cocoa provide not only superb flavours, but plenty of detail to appreciate and to sustain interest. Far from ordinary. **Fruition Chocolate say** Big vanilla and caramel notes round out this interpretation of a classic. **Cacao** Environmentally friendly and fairly traded, from the Acopagro co-operative in San Martin, Peru. **Established** In November 2011 by Bryan Graham, who attributes his interest in baking and pastry to his grandmother. Through visits to her farm, Bryan learnt how to pick perfectly ripe ingredients and transform them into pies, tarts, jams and jellies. Aged sixteen, Bryan became a baking and pastry apprentice at the Bear Café. At eighteen he was promoted to Pastry Chef. Five years later, Bryan continued his education at the Culinary Institute of America, in New York. He completed his externship at Jacques Torres Chocolates. But it was when Bryan made chocolate from bean to bar with Chef Peter Greweling that he became interested in the art of chocolate making. **Made** In the store and workshop in Shokan, Catskill Mountains, New York State.

Milk chocolate Blended with vanilla.

●●●Sweet ●●Cocoa ●●Milk ●●Vanilla ●●Butter

Taste Almond; amaretti; biscuit; hazelnut; light caramel; chocolate cake; roast; malt; blueberry. Hint of smoke and halva.

Dark Milk Chocolate with Fleur de Sel

Fruition Chocolate ✿ ✿

Profoundly rich and satisfying flavours are released as this chocolate slowly melts. There are innumerable notes in the low to mid-range, but this chocolate is also special because of the way its base notes finish on (not before) the line where bitterness starts. A similar thing happens at the opposite end of the scale: the notes go high enough to allow dark hints of fruit on the boundary with acidity. The salt is consistent and superbly enhances the other ingredients in this dark, exotic, bar. But it is strong enough to be appreciated. **Fruition Chocolate say** Straddling the line between light and dark, and fused with fleur de sel. **Cacao** From Costa Rica. **Interestingly** Bryan Graham crafts very small batches of chocolate of only thirty five or forty kilos. Unusually, all roasting is done in a simple convection oven on perforated sheet pans. "It's not the most efficient method, but I've been able to get excellent and consistent results," he explained.

Milk chocolate Blended with vanilla and salt.

●●●Cocoa ●●Salt ●●Sweet ●Milk ●Vanilla ●Butter ●Sour

Taste Liquorice; treacle; rye bread; anise; whole milk; flower; deep roast; dark cherry; raspberry. Hint of nut, malt and coffee.

FRUITION CHOCOLATE CACAOFÉVIER WWW.TASTEFRUITION.COM

349

MILK CHOCOLATE

Jacques Torres ✿ ✿

A tasty and refined interpretation of classic milk chocolate with a very endearing and distinctive flavour profile. It is playful, yet has remarkably gratifying tender tones of cocoa and creamy milk to relish. **Jacques says** Deliciously smooth and creamy. This is what milk chocolate should taste like. It's a rich creamy flavour (none of that spoilt milk taste normally found in milk chocolates) blended with dark chocolate. Yummy! **Established** In 2000, with the opening of a factory, with store, in the DUMBO area of Brooklyn. In 2004, he opened his second chocolate factory in a flagship store on Hudson Street, in downtown New York. There are no tours, but visitors to the retail area can view the action through the glass walls. There are now six Jacques Torres shops in New York, all of which are decorated in the colours of the cacao pod. **Made** In New York. **Interestingly** Jacques' story started when he was twenty years old: on a bet, he audaciously walked into the kitchen of Nice's most famous hotel, the Negresco, and asked Michelin two-star chef Jacques Maximin for a job. Maximin gave him an hour to return to work with a chef's coat. Jacques used his days off during eight years at the Negresco to go to school and earn a Master Pastry Chef degree. In 1988 he moved to the United States to work as Corporate Pastry Chef at the Ritz Carlton Hotel Company, and went on to work at New York's most famous restaurant, Le Cirque. During his time at Le Cirque, Jacques made fifty two episodes of "Dessert Circus" for television, and released two companion cookbooks. He also hosted a television series, "Chocolate with Jacques Torres," on the Food Network for three years. Jacques has also carried out consulting and product development for Valrhona and Cointreau. Jacques, who's nickname is Mr Chocolate, is married to Hasty Torres, a fellow chocolatier who has her own chocolate shop in Beverly Hills, called Madame Chocolat.

Milk chocolate Blended with vanilla.

●●●Milk ●●●Sweet ●●Cocoa ●●Butter ●Vanilla

Taste Caramel; chocolate ice cream; creamy malted milkshake; roast nut. Hint of salt.

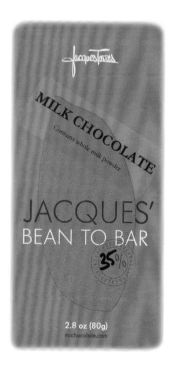

JACQUES' BEAN TO BAR 35%

Jacques Torres ✤

A distinctive chocolate because of its mature, sophisticated, yet sweet and creamy, tangy flavours. The complexity develops deliciously as it melts, providing plenty of distractions. **Jacques Torres says** Using beans from the Dominican Republic, Jacques roasted, conched and moulded them into these deliciously creamy milk chocolate bars. **Cacao** From the Dominican Republic. **Pictured** Above: Jacques creates a chocolate cage by slowly deflating a balloon over which he has drizzled chocolate and refrigerated to harden it. Right: in October 2011 the director and original cast of "Willy Wonka and the Chocolate Factory" gathered at Jacques Torres to celebrate the 40th anniversary of the movie and promote a new collector's edition of it. Oompa Loompas took to the streets of New York, to hand out Golden Tickets for the event.

Milk chocolate Blended with vanilla.

●●●Milk   ●●●Cocoa 35%   ●●Sweet   ●●Butter   ●Vanilla

Taste Tobacco; almond; walnut; raisin; toffee; vanilla fudge; olive; whole milk. Hint of hay and smoke.

DARK MILK

Patric Chocolate ✿ ✿

Although accompanied by the finest cream, the cocoa retains its potency and provides long-lasting, fully-loaded flavours with profound hues that will satisfy the darkest cravings. **Patric says** Milk chocolate can't be world class? Who says? This dark milk chocolate allows the beauty of Patric's signature cacao blend to shine, subtly softened with notes of fresh, creamy, sweet milk, and much less sugar than your average milk chocolate bar. This is truly a milk chocolate unlike any other. **Established** In July 2007, after cacao sourcing trips to Central and South America plus months of careful development, Alan McClure, 28, released his first chocolate bar. Allan, who used his middle name for the brand, became inspired during a year spent in France, where Valrhona and Bernachon made a impression on him. The scarcity of fine chocolate upon his return to the States was another motivation. In addition to blends and single origin chocolates, Patric is also known for their exciting limited editions: micro-batches of only a few hundred bars with adventurous flavours. **Made** In Columbia, Missouri, the United States of America. The workshop is not open to the public, but local retailers include HyVee, Root Cellar, World Harvest and Clover's. **Interestingly** Patric are one of very few cacaofèviers in the world who roast the cacao in a convection oven. "Because the beans don't tumble, it results in no breakage and zero charred or over-roasted bits." Allan explained. Pictured opposite: the chocolate is poured into warm plastic moulds, which are then placed onto a vibrating table. This settles the thick chocolate evenly flat and causes any trapped air in the corners to escape, leaving a perfect bar, ready to be cooled, then wrapped.

Milk chocolate.

●●●Cocoa ●●Milk ●Sweet ●Butter ●Bitter

Taste Dark chocolate cake; red fruit; walnut; almond; malt; molasses; wood; sesame; honey; cream. Hint of salt and tea.

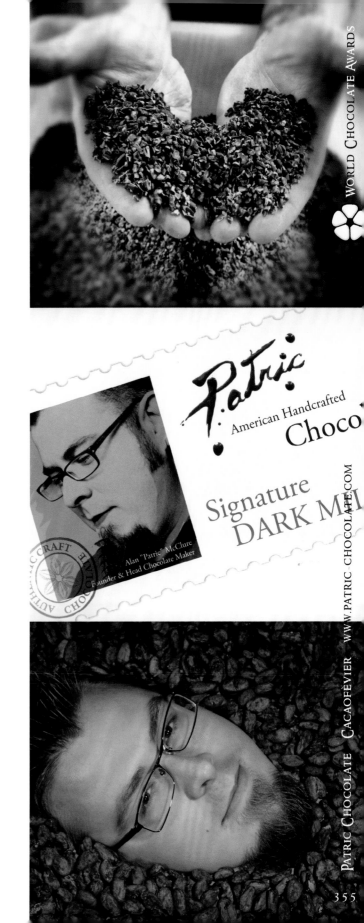

Alan "Patric" McClure
Founder & Head Chocolate Maker

Patric
American Handcrafted
Choco

Signature
DARK MI

CAPPUCCINO OMG

Patric Chocolate ⊗ ⊗

Gentle and composed: an elegantly creamy espresso, sensitively sweetened. The cocoa butter is free from vanilla, allowing clean, complex flavours to flourish. Fine texture and a perfect balance of quality ingredients make this original bar a classic. **Patric say** Our "like-nothing-you've-ever-tasted" Cappuccino OMG [oh my god] bar: we hold the cacao and let the craft-roasted espresso and creamy whole milk do the talking! It's like a cup of cappuccino in bar form. One of our best selling bars! **Interestingly** COMG is made with an award-winning Espresso 700 coffee from a local company called Kaldi. It's a blend of beans from Central and South America. **Pictured** Right: Allan on a cacao sourcing expedition in Venezuela and a pod growing from the trunk of rare variety of criollo cacao tree called porcelana. The Spanish named it after the ceramic because of its remarkable white cacao beans.

White chocolate Blended with coffee beans.

●●Milk   ●●Butter   ●●Coffee   ●Sweet

Taste Whole milk; cream; butter; finely roasted coffee.

357

EXTRA RICH MILK

Scharffen Berger ✿ ✿ ✿

This isn't milk chocolate: it is vanilla milk chocolate. This is a bar with smooth texture, with an emphasis on the sweet floral vanilla and full-bodied cocoa. Both elements work together beautifully: they are exceptional in quality and in range of notes. **Scharffen Berger say** With hints of luxurious caramel, our 41% cacao milk chocolate is as rich as it is creamy. **Cacao** Made from a proprietary blend of beans sourced from up to nine different cacao-growing regions around the world. **Established** In 1997 in San Francisco by chocolate connoisseur Robert Steinberg (right) and wine maker John Scharffenberger (left). The venture started in Robert's kitchen with a few simple kitchen appliances and nearly thirty varieties of cacao to experiment with. Robert was a family doctor diagnosed with lymphoma in 1989. It proved to be a life-changing experience, and he decided to dedicate himself to his passion for fine food, settling on chocolate making from 1994 until the end of his life in 2008. Robert's skills were complimented by John's entrepreneurial spirit, successful business background, and astute palate. "I've never been with someone who is more demanding about nuances of flavour and aroma. We would sit down and sometimes taste forty different cacao and twenty different liquors he had made. We'd go through thirty or forty iterations of sweetness levels." John recalled. The duo initially focused on supplying chocolate to chefs, but had little success due to fierce competition and price sensitivity. Before funds ran out, they recognised that public demand was strong. John hired a stall one Saturday at the local farmer's market. He sold over $3000 of chocolate bars. Robert had the same experience the following weekend. It wasn't long until Scharffen Berger was on the shelves nationwide in retailers such as Whole Foods. In 2005 the Hershey Company acquired Scharffen Berger through the Artisan Confections Company, a wholly owned subsidiary, making a firm commitment to uphold the company's chocolate making traditions. **Made** In Robinson, Illinois, since 2009 when Scharffen Berger closed its Berkeley California plant (lower right). The original small-batch chocolate making process using vintage European equipment has been preserved to this day.

Milk chocolate Blended with vanilla.

●●Cocoa 41%　●●Sweet　●●Milk　●●Vanilla　●Butter　●Bitter

Taste Set honey; buttered toast; malt; whole milk; thick caramel; dark chocolate cake; cream soda.

NET WT 3 OZ (85g)

MILK NIBBY

Scharffenberger ⊗ ⊗

Everybody has been invited to the party. It's smooth and it's crunchy; it's creamy and it's got gutsy cocoa; it's got sweet vanilla and a hint of salt. And they are all partying on your taste buds like rock stars. **Scharffen Berger say** The luxurious caramel richness of our milk chocolate, united with the delicious and crunchy texture of roasted cacao bean nib. **Cacao** A blend of up to nine origins. **Interestingly** Fortunately co-founder Robert Steinberg did not give up when manufacturers in the United States declined to share information about making chocolate with him. He wrote to Bernachon, a small family-owned chocolate maker in Lyon, France. "I was nearly certain they would say no, and I still don't understand why they agreed, but whatever the reason, I think I glowed when the fax came through saying I could spend two weeks working there. It's safe to say that without Bernachon, there probably wouldn't be any Scharffen Berger." **Pictured** The bar and wrapper feature an ibex mountain goat, taken from the Scharffenberger family crest. The family name is split into two words in order to avoid any connection with the wine brand that John previously founded.

Milk chocolate Blended with vanilla. Scattered with cocoa nibs on one side.

●●●Cocoa 41%   ●●Sweet   ●●Milk   ●●Vanilla   ●Bitter

Taste Bourbon cream biscuit; caramel; salt; nougat; crunchy cocoa nib.

SeriousMilk™
MILK CHOCOLATE
"CACAO"
lush and fudgy
53% Cacao
Organic & Fair Trade
2oz (58 g)

chocolate is to cacao as wine i

CACAO

TCHO

"Cacao" is true to its name: an uncomplicated extra-dark milk chocolate, with an emphasis on deep cocoa flavours and cream. Its texture is very smooth, allowing it to melt beautifully, before leaving you with a slightly dry aftertaste of roasted cocoa to savour. **TCHO say** [Cacao] dances along the tantalising boundary between the finest dark chocolate and rich, indulgent milk chocolate. Bold cacao richness is delicately balanced with subtle cream and warm caramel notes. Reminiscent of a rich dark chocolate ice cream - in a bar. Our chocolate maker Brad Kintzer says, "It is a complex blend of notes, starting with the underlying cacao, then including the creaminess of milk and the caramel tones that heating milk creates." **Cacao** Trinitario from Peru and Ecuador. **Established** In 2005 by Timothy Childs (right) a NASA space shuttle contractor, and Karl Bittong, who had four decades of experience designing and building chocolate manufacturing plants, and developing formulations for leading producers, including Bensdorp, Transmar, Van Houten and Unilever. In 2007, Wired magazine co-founder Louis Rossetto (left) joined as CEO. **Made** In San Francisco, California. **Interestingly** TCHO is a phonetic spelling of the first syllable of the word chocolate.

Milk chocolate Blended with vanilla.

●●●Cocoa 53%   ●●Butter   ●●Sweet   ●Milk   ●Vanilla

Taste Butter; coconut; roast; liquorice; molasses; fudge; coffee; drop of cream.

TCHO
Pier 17
San Francisco, C
www.TCHO.com

TCHO Cacaofévier www.tcho.com

SALTED ALMOND

Theo ⊛

The flavoursome qualities of the cocoa blend, which range from rich and chocolaty to light and fine, can be savoured whilst enjoying the bold salt, rounded vanilla and gentle almond. Very moreish. **Theo say** Seductively rich and creamy milk chocolate with the irresistible crunch of almonds, with just the right amount of pink Himalayan salt! **Established** In March of 2006 Theo created their first batch of chocolate, from the beans, after founder Joseph Whinney and his team converted a quaint old brewery building into the first organic chocolate factory in the United States. Complete with a cast-iron 1937 German ball roaster and a bar-wrapping machine from the sixties. **Made** In Seattle, Washington state. The factory has a shop and provides tours by advance booking.

Milk chocolate Blended with vanilla and salt. Containing almond nibs.

●●●Salt ●●Cocoa 45% ●●Sweet ●●Milk ●●Butter ●Almond ●Vanilla

Taste Chocolate; brownie; whole milk; vanilla; light roast almond; caramel; salt. Hint of flower and malt.

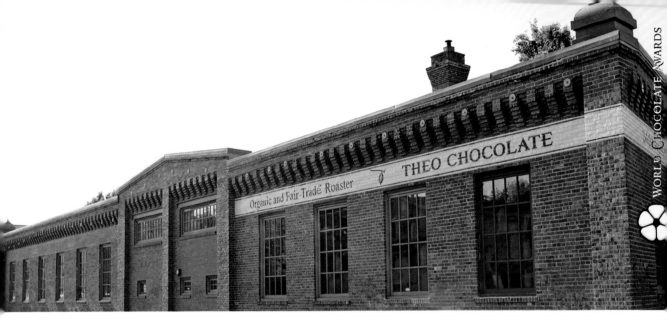

COCONUT CURRY

Theo ⊗

An exuberant celebration of the exotic markets of India: playful yellow curry, warming spices, plus the tender flavours and texture of coconut almost leap out from the exceptional, wholesome chocolate. **Theo say** Milk chocolate with toasted coconut and savoury curry spices. Theo takes its premium quality, delectable chocolate and combines it with some bold and traditional ingredients to conjure an assortment of fantasy flavours. **Interestingly** Theo toast the unsweetened organic coconut flakes in-house.

Milk chocolate Blended with yellow curry powder and vanilla. Containing small shreds of coconut.

••Hot Spice   ••Mild Spice   ••Cocoa 45%   ••Coconut   ••Sweet   ••Milk   ••Vanilla   •Butter

Taste Coriander; turmeric; coconut; mustard; paprika; red pepper; cardamom; nutmeg; cinnamon; clove; vanilla.

367

CHAI TEA

Theo ⊗ ⊗

Cinnamon and then clove lead, followed by tea and other gentle flavours that provide intrigue in the background. Warm and soothing sensations are enjoyed bite after bite. Theo's distinctive vanilla milk chocolate is the base. A must-have for cinnamon lovers. **Theo say** Milk chocolate with a warming blend of chai spices and loose leaf organic black tea. **Interestingly** The name Theo is a truncation of the botanical name for the cacao tree: Theobroma cacao. "This name was chosen to remind folks who eat our chocolate that it is made from the roasted, fermented beans from the pods of the cacao tree. Loosing touch on where one's food comes from is not a good thing and our company is built around educating people about good chocolate." Explained Andy McShea of Theo. **Pictured** Theo's factory is colour-coded: yellow indicates apparatus through which the cacao moves from one place to another; green highlights machinery for processing the cacao into chocolate, such as the winnower (top right, and centre right, opposite the ball roaster, also featured on the opposite page.) The roasted cacao beans are crushed once, breaking them into nibs, then the winnower's five vibrating decks separate the nibs from the shells.

Milk chocolate Blended with vanilla, tea, clove, cinnamon and cardamom.

●●Cocoa 45%   ●●Sweet   ●●Milk   ●●Spice
●●Butter   ●Tea

Taste Cinnamon; clove; ginger; cardamom; cream; milk; chocolate cake; caramel; vanilla.

THEO CHOCOLATE CACAOFEVIER WWW.THEOCHOCOLATE.COM

ORGANIC MILK CHOCOLATE

Theo & Jane Goodall ⊗

Cocoa, milk and vanilla all compete for your attention in this rich and lively chocolate. A remarkably wide range of light to dark cocoa flavours are present, owing to this particular blend of beans. **Theo say** Creamy and delicious milk chocolate bar, organic and Fair Trade certified. **Interestingly** "We give a product like chocolate to each other to show how much we care about each other, but the people who are producing the crop have a life expectancy of forty five years and their children are illiterate and malnourished..." Observed Joe Whinney, who founded Theo in order to address such issues. The chocolatier's partnership with Jane Goodall is inspired by "Cocoa Practices" a ground-breaking Theo initiative that brings together small scale cacao farmers, larger producers and non-governmental organisations from the world's cacao producing regions. Cocoa Practices is designed to give farmers the tools they need to grow high-quality cacao beans whilst conserving wildlife and other natural resources in the rainforest eco-systems that provide both their livelihoods and their homes. Proceeds from the sale of this chocolate help cocoa farmers, rainforest conservation, efforts to save chimpanzees, community centred conservation efforts, and youth education programs worldwide.

Milk chocolate Blended with vanilla.

●●●Cocoa 45%   ●●●Vanilla   ●●Sweet   ●●Milk   ●●Butter

Taste Vanilla ice cream; sherbet; dark chocolate cake; malt; caramel; orange; spice; wood. Hint of smoke.

LATTE MOCHA
Vintage Plantations ⊗ ⊗

A melody of delicate coffee, dairy and nutty chocolate notes. They fuse flawlessly, bringing out the best in each other. Latte Mocha is a laid-back, elegant, way to experience coffee, but with enough flavour for it to be relished. Expect an occasional, gentle, crunch of coffee too. **Vintage Plantations say** For all the chocolate lovers who order lattes at the coffee shop. We've infused certified AA Ethiopian arabica mild-roast coffee, ground with our milk chocolate along with tiny amounts of instant coffee, which defuses in the milk chocolate as it is being slowly tempered. The result is a creamy bar, with a balanced taste of coffee and milk vying for your attention, and the crunchiness of tiny pieces of coffee beans - the closest thing to "a latte on the go." **Cacao** Forastero Nacional from Ecuador. **Established** In 1993. Vintage Plantations was born out of the friendship of two rugby players: Pierrick Chouard and Allan Suarez. Allan was the founder of a social networking web portal. Pierrick has been in the chocolate industry since 1985. He studied tropical agriculture in Paris, and was recruited by Mars for cocoa liquor sourcing before his graduation. After moving to the marketing side of the business, he went on to work with Neuhaus, then launched Café-Tasse, then Michel Cluizel in the USA. He was also instrumental in pioneering the Rainforest Alliance cocoa program. Pierrick and Allan created a "University of Chocolate" program to educate chocolate professionals about the challenges farmers of high quality cacao have in the Dominican Republic, and Ecuador. Next, they decided to make chocolate in the country of origin, Ecuador, which proved a challenging period with many setbacks. Nowadays the cacao beans are shipped to the USA to be roasted in-house. **Made** In Newark, New Jersey.

Milk chocolate Containing with minute coffee nibs and instant coffee.

●●●Butter ●●Milk ●●Sweet ●●Coffee ●●Cocoa 38%

Taste Latte mocha; caramel; crème brulèe; mascarpone; cookie dough; roast chestnut. Hint of hazelnut and peanut.

MILK WITH ROASTED PEANUTS

Vintage Plantations ✣ ✣

A carefully measured, but fun, composition: gracious sweet, nutty flavours and a generous portion of milk, complimented intermittently by superb gentle peanuts. **Vintage Plantations say** Bringing you back to the traditional way of making milk chocolate. The flavour is long and nutty, with a powerful dominant chocolate note, no bitterness, little acidity, and some tannins. **Cacao** Nacional from Ecuador. **Pictured** Jenny of Vintage Plantations checking fermented and dried beans at Rancho Grande, Vince, Los Rios province, before they are collected and shipped to the workshop in the United States. Above: a view of the natural habitat of the cacao tree, where the forest canopy provides essential shade for young seedlings.

Milk chocolate Containing whole and half peanuts.

●●●Milk ●●Sweet ●●Cocoa 38% ●●Butter ●Peanut

Taste Whole milk; light roast peanut; almond; honey; nougat; caramel. Hint of coffee and cashew.

VINTAGE PLANTATIONS · CACAOPEVIER · VINTAGEPLANTATIONS.COM

VINTAGE
plantations
Milk Chocolate
with Roasted Peanuts

375

WHOLE MILK

Net Weight 100g (3.5oz)

WHOLE MILK

Vintage Plantations ⊗ ⊗ ⊗

As it melts away smoothly, a very endearing and impressive nutty character is revealed. This is accompanied by rich fresh milk and rounded caramel... a recipe for relaxing moments. This is a gentle, easy-going, flavoursome chocolate, free from aggression, yet full of character. **Vintage Plantations say** Bringing you back to the traditional way of making milk chocolate. The flavour is long and nutty, with a powerful dominant chocolate note, no bitterness, little acidity, and some tannins. **Cacao** Nacional from Ecuador. **Interestingly** "In 1996 we noticed that the major barrier to increasing the quality of the chocolate was the farmer. Few had ever eaten a chocolate bar and had no idea what was becoming of the cocoa beans they had sold to the local middle-man." Says co-founder Pierrick Chouard. "To make good chocolate, we deemed it was essential to get the farmers to understand how important fermentation was. We taught them the basics of fermentation and introduced them to the end product - the chocolate bar made with their cocoa beans." Vintage Plantations also pay cacao farmers directly. **Pictured** Pierrick inspects cacao beans which have already been fermented and are to be laid out to dry in the heat of the sun for several days. The beans are turned over with wooden rakes or shovels from time to time, to promote drying. Metal tools can harm the beans, which need to remain intact. In the background is a structure to shelter the beans from rainstorms, or the intensity of the mid-day sun. The purpose of drying is to halt fermentation and prepare the beans for transportation to the chocolate factory by reducing their water content from about 50% to 6-7%. Any less and the beans would be too brittle; much higher and the beans might end up mouldy. After drying, the beans are packed into jute sacks ready for delivery.

Milk chocolate.

●●●Milk ●●Sweet ●●Cocoa 38% ●●Butter

Taste Whole milk; hazelnut; peanut; almond; lavender; flower; sultana; dark sugar; caramel; fig; butter; coconut; gingerbread.

PURCHASING CHOCOLATE

AVAILABILITY	Some chocolates are produced in batches and can become temporarily unavailable.

WEBSITES	Each brand's website may be found listed on the right edge of the right page. Some brands do not update their websites regularly, or list their complete range of products online. Other online retailers may be found by using a search engine, or by contacting the brand or its distributor in your country. An email or telephone call may be required to make international orders.

SHOPS	Chocolate retailers may be found by using a search engine, or by contacting the brand or its distributor in your country. Some brands have their own shops which are sometimes located at the factory site.

OUTLET An outlet is a shop attached to a factory or warehouse that offers products to the public at special prices. Generally their opening hours are short and they open only on certain days of the week. Outlets for brands in this guide book are listed below.

Australia Haigh's, Adelaide, South Australia.

England Hotel Chocolat, Huntingdon, Cambridgeshire.
Red Star Chocolate, Cleethorpes, Lincolnshire.

France Michel Cluizel, Damville, Upper Normandy.

Germany Coppeneur, Bad Honnef, Rhein-Sieg.
Meybona, Löhne, North Rhine-Westphalia.
Rausch, Peine, Lower Saxony.
Stollwerck (manufacturer of Sarotti) Saalfeld, Thuringia.

Switzerland Maestrani, Flawil, St. Gallen.

Italy Domori and Leone, Turin, Piedmont.

United States of America Michel Cluizel, West Berlin, New Jersey.

CALL AND COLLECT Some factories do not have a shop or outlet, but allow orders placed in advance by telephone or email to be collected. Minimum quantities may apply.

Brazil Amma, Salvador, Bahia.

England Artisan du Chocolat, Ashford, Kent.

Italy Amedei, Pontedera, Tuscany.

EVENTS	Many of the brands listed in the guide are present at food or chocolate fairs around the world. Contact the brand or its distributor in your country for details.

Index of Ingredients

A list of chocolates and the page numbers on which they are found, in order of key ingredient. For food allergy related information always consult the manufacturer and the label of the product.

Orange Marcolini: Breakfast 72. Bernachon: Orange 146. Ducasse: Amandes 182. Coppeneur: Orangenöl & Urwaldpfeffer 211

Passion fruit Caoni: Passion Fruit 98
Peanut Vintage: Roasted Peanuts 374
Peppercorn, Dolfin: Masala 53. Coppeneur: Orangenöl & Urwaldpfeffer 211. Macstrani: Erdbeer 325. Theo: Chai Tea 369
Pine nut Ducasse: Amandes 182
Pistachio Gerbaud: Pistaches 56. Marcolini: Five O'Clock 65. Ducasse: Amandes 182. Amedei: Bianco Pistacchi 247, Quadrotti Pistacchi 254. Leone: Pistachio 272. Vestri: Bianco Pistacchi 295. Askinosie: White Pistachios 338

Rasberry Maestrani: Himbeer 323
Rice Marcolini: Breakfast 72. Vivani: Crisp 231
Rose Rococo: Rose Otto 134

Salt, as a flavouring Gerbaud: Pistaches 56, Lait 58, Noisettes 60. Rope: Lemon 103, Hazelnut 104, Lime 107. Hotel: Salt 118, Salt & Caramel 122. Cluizel: Éclats 168. Ducasse: Ivoire 180. Coppeneur: Karamell & Sal 216. Domori: Lattesal 268. Rivoire: Latte 276. Askinosie: Pistachios 338, Licorice 340, Sel 337. Fruition: Sel 348. Theo: Almond 365
Salt, as a seasoning Zotter: Erdbeer Kokos 39, Kuvertüre 40, Nicaragua 42. Marcolini: Lait 62, Java 66, Sans 69, Blanc 71. Bernachon: Nature 140
Sheep milk Choco-Lina: Bourbon Vanille 29
Strawberry Zotter: Erdbeer Kokos 39
Sugar, no added Tiroler Edle: 48% Ohne 33, 70% Ohne 31. Marcolini: Sans 69. Bonnat: Sans 158
Sultanas Vestri: Bianco Uvetta 293

Tea Café-Tasse: Jasmine Tea & Violet Extracts 47. Dolfin: Rooibush 51. Hotel: Earl Grey 125. Roux: Yuzu Macha 200. Theo: Chai Tea 369
Tomato Rovira: Pizza 313
Tonka bean Artisan: Tonka 111

Vanilla in milk chocolate Haigh's: Milk 22. Zotter: Nicaragua 42. Marcolini: Lait 62. Dolfin: Ghana 55. Cotton: Dark 76, Nibs 78, Light 80. Ixcacao: Light 84. Hotel: Milk 50% 127. Rococo: Organic 132. Cluizel: Lait 173, Mangaro 176, Maralumi 178. Ducasse: Ivoire 180. Coppeneur: Madagascar 219, Ecuador 220. Hachez: Wild 45% 223. Meybona: Papua 224. Rausch: Guácimo 227. Danta: Acacias 236, Ujuxtes 235. Amedei: Brown 249. Leone: Latte 271. Slitti: 45% 285, 51% 287, 62% 289, 70% 290. Naive: Organic 298. Madécasse: Milk 302. Menakao: Milk 305. Maestrani: Doppel 326. Amano: Ocumare 330. Fruition: Classic 346. Escazú: Goat's 344. Torres: Milk 350, Bean 35% 352. Scharffen Berger: Rich 359, Nibby 360. TCHO: Cacao 362. Theo: Organic 370
Violet Café-Tasse: Jasmine Tea & Violet 47

White chocolate Choco-Lina: Bourbon 29. Marcolini: Blanc 71. Goss: White 83. Willie's: Blanco 136. Bonnat: Ivoire 161. Cluizel: Ivoire 175. Coppeneur: Dominicana 208, Madagascar 219. Sarotti: Weisse Damen 229. Danta: Blanco 239. Amedei: White 245. Askinosie: White 333
White chocolate with added ingredients Zotter: Erdbeer Kokos 39. Vivani: Crisp 231. Danta: Trocitos 241. Amedei: Pistacchi 247. Domori: Biancomenta 261, Biancoliquirizia 262, Cappuccino 265. Vestri: Pistacchi 295, Uvetta 293. Rovira: Pizza 313. Maestrani: Himbeer 323, Erdbeer 325. Askinosie: Nibble 334, Pistachios 338
Wild cacao Morin: Bolvie 40% 188, Bolvie 48% 190. Hachez: Wild 45% 223

Yoghurt Vivani: Crisp 231

Yuzu Roux: Yuzu Macha 200

IMAGE CREDITS

All images are copyright and may not be reproduced without the permission of their owner.

ALTER ECO Open cacao beans during and after fermentation (FHIA Honduras) with the assistance of Aroldo Dubon; chocolate packaging **World Chocolate Awards**. All other images **Alter Eco**.

AMELIA ROPE Pale Lime & Sea Salt bar packaging isolated **World Chocolate Awards**. Lemon tree **ODM/Shutterstock.com**. Maldon sea salt sacks; harvesting Maldon sea salt; ancient sea salt harvest site **Maldon Crystal Salt/Maldonsalt.co.uk**. All other images **Amelia Rope**.

AMMA F. Schilling (Salon du Chocolat Paris) **Evert-Jan/Choqoa.com**. All other images, excluding isolated packaging **Amma**.

AMANO Portrait of Art Pollard **Amano**.

AMEDEI *Toscano Brown* Chocolate bar packaging *Toscano White* Chocolate bar packaging background **Sarunyu_foto/Shutterstock.com**. Cecilia Tessieri; Amedei Pralines open and closed boxes **Amedei**. *Toscano Nut Brown Gianduja* Cecilia **Amedei**. *Latte con Nocciole* All images, excluding chocolate bar packaging **Amedei**. *Cioccolato Bianco con Pistacchi* Chocolate bar packaging **Amedei**. *Quadrotti Toscani Ripieno di Pistachi e Granella di Cacao* Cecilia; pralines in open box; packing Armonie Toscane pralines **Amedei**. *Quadrotti Toscani Cioccolato al Latte e Crema Toscana* Cecilia; filled chocolates in white frilled wrappers, Quadrotti Toscani boxes **Amedei**. *Crema Toscana Nocciola* Cecilia **Amedei**.

ARTISAN DU CHOCOLAT 1799 map of West Indies and Caribbean Sea **Steven Wright/Shutterstock.com**. Tonka beans **Tom Grundy/Shutterstock.com**. Bunch of cut lemongrass **Buifong/Shutterstock.com**. Lemongrass bush (Thailand) **Satit_srihin/Shutterstock.com**. Ginger **Fuchi/Shutterstock.com**. Panama and Jamaica chocolate boxes; cacao pod illustration; coins; Declaration of Feelings **World Chocolate Awards**. All other images **Artisan du Chocolat**.

ASKINOSIE "How Our Chocolate is Made" poster **Askinosie (design by Kristina Sacci kristinasacci.com)**. White Chocolate bar background **Subbotina Anna/Shutterstock.com**. Davao bar background **Vladitto/Shutterstock.com**. Santa Cruz falls (Mindanao) **Leksele/Shutterstock.com**. Valley (Mindanao) **Chris Howey/Shutterstock.com**. Text close up on Davao bar packaging **Lee McCoy/Chocolatiers.co.uk** All chocolate bar packaging; White Chocolate Nibble bar **World Chocolate Awards**. All other images **Askinosie**.

BERNACHON Mr Dauvet and Philippe Bernachon **BONY/Gamma-Rapho/Getty Images**. Bernachon family; cacao in sack **Bernachon**.

BONNAT Stéphane Bonnat **Bonnat**. Placing bars on display **Evert-Jan/choqoa.com**. Illustrations **Jampur Fraize facebook.com/jampurfraize**.

CAFÉ TASSE Shop exterior; wood box; chocolate bar packaging **World Chocolate Awards**. Jasmine flowering **Miramiska/Shutterstock.com**. All other images **Café-Tasse**.

CAONI
All chocolate bar packaging; wood box **World Chocolate Awards**. San Rafael Falls **Dr. Morley Read/Shutterstock.com**. Cocoa beans background of wood box **Sklep Spozywczy/Shutterstock.com**. Roasted macadamia nuts **Jeehyun**. Macadamia nuts on tree **Joloei**. Passion fruit **Oliver Hoffmann/Shutterstock.com**. Passion fruit pulp **Nir Darom/Shutterstock.com**.

CHAPON All images **Chapon**.

CHOCOLINA Single sheep **Bestweb/Shutterstock.com**. Flock of sheep with shepherd **Mircea Bezergheanu/Shutterstock.com**.

CLUIZEL MICHEL Mangaro cacao beans in sack; chocolate tasting samples (Salon du Chocolat, Paris) **Evert-Jan/choqoa.com**. Hazelnuts on branch **Geanina Bechea/Shutterstock.com**. Making caramel **Foodpictures/Shutterstock.com**. All isolated chocolate bar packaging; Champignons; shop (Paris); vase; bow tied box; chocolate baguettes; strawberry nougat and chocolate stones. **World Chocolate Awards**. Huts (PNG) **Tyler Olson/Shutterstock.com**. PNG ariel view **Byelikova Oksana/Shutterstock.com**. All other images **Michel Cluizel**.

COPPENEUR Plantation, wildlife; cocoa tree, loading boat, harvest, fermentation boxes (Madagascar) **Coppeneur**. Coppeneur workshop (Bad Honnef); Coppeneur shop (Bonn); chocolate bar, chocolate bar boxes **World Chocolate Awards**.

COTTON TREE Cocoa beans on scales at Cotton Tree **Nancy Buchman**. Cacao pods on tree trunk (Toldeo) **Bruno Kuppinger/Toledo Cave & Adventure Tours**. Light Milk with Cocoa Nibs packaging and bar **World Chocolate Awards**. Light Milk with Cocoa Nibs packaging background **Manasapat/Shutterstock.com**. All other images **Juli Puryear**.

DANTA All images of Finca Los Ujuxtes **Richard Tango-Lowy/Dancinglionchocolate.com**. Domed yellow church (Antigua Guatemala) **Mike Cohen/Shutterstock.com**. Danta (animal) **Ammit/Shutterstock.com**. Bonbons **Danta**. Mayan glyphs (Qurigua, Guatemala) **Vladimir Korostyshevskiy/Shutterstock.com**.

DOLFIN Rooibush tea **World Chocolate Awards**. Landscape (Cederberg) **Jon Wade**. Split rock formation, (Cederberg) **Jim Sher/**

Shutterstock.com. Indian market spices **Girish Menon/Shutterstock.com**. Rooftops **PBorowka/Shutterstock.com**. Nougat **Soare Cecilia Corina/Shutterstock.com**. Almond tree blossoming **Bomshtein/Shutterstock.com**. Almond nuts unripe on branch **Nito/Shutterstock.com**. Almond orchard **AndrusV/Shutterstock.com**. Ripe almonds on branch **Neftali/Shutterstock.com**. Almonds unshelled **Balefire/Shutterstock.com**. Almonds shelled **Kiselev Andrey Valerevich/Shutterstock.com**.

DOMORI Guerande salt ponds **Pack-Shot/Shutterstock.com**. Gianluca Franzoni inspecting nibs; Biancoliquirizia bar; Cacao Cult sign; ball mill; jute sack close up; Cacao San Jose sacks; cocoa butter melt; Gianluca and colleague walking in warehouse; Gianluca with Domori sensory chart; TFC 400; cocoa nibs in white sack; Gianluca inspecting chocolate tank **World Chocolate Awards**. All other images **Domori**.

DUCASSE ALAIN LE CHOCOLAT Copper background **Luba V Nel**.

ENRIC ROVIRA All images, excluding Amaretti chocolate box **Enric Rovira**.

ESCAZÚ All images, excluding chocolate bar packaging **Escazú**.

FRIIS HOLM Mikkel Friis-Holm **Chloe/Faerietalefoodie.com**. Wood background **Sunny Forest/Shutterstock.com**.

FRUITION CHOCOLATE All images, excluding chocolate bar packaging **Fruition Chocolate**.

GOSS Crushing cocoa beans into nibs (Toldeo) **Nancy Buchman**. Roasting cacao (Toldeo); winnowing (Toldeo) **Bruno Kuppinger/Toledo Cave & Adventure Tours**.

HACHEZ All images **Hachez**.

HAIGHS CHOCOLATES Haigh's vintage car **Marilyn**. All images, excluding Milk Peppermint chocolate bar packaging **Haigh's Chocolates**.

HOTEL CHOCOLAT The Pitons and town (Saint Lucia) **Nina B/Shutterstock.com**. Close up of grafting cacao (FHIA, Honduras) with the assistance of Aroldo Dubon; heart chocolate boxes; cacao pod; "Britain" brochure cover; butterfly bag **World Chocolate Awards**. Charles Grey 2nd Earl Grey painted by Thomas Phillips **National Portrait Gallery, London**. All other images **Hotel Chocolat**.

IXCACAO MAYA BELIZEAN CHOCOLATE Chocolate bar packaging **World Chocolate Awards**. All other images **Susan Klos**.

JACQUES TORRES Oompa Loompas and Jacques Torres **Cindy Ord/Getty Images**. Willy Wonka & The Chocolate Factory cast and director with Jacques Torres **John Lamparski/Getty Images**. Jacques Torres holding chocolate heart **Stan Honda/AFP/Getty Images**. Heart gift box **Kimberly Vardeman**. Cutting chocolate cake **Rachel Kramer Bussel**. Chocolate and nut slabs on display **Jill M**. Jacques Torres Chocolate signs **Ema Martins**. Jacques Torres chocolate cage demonstration **Steven Tom**.

MADÉCASSE Oxcart passing baobab trees (Madagascar) **Marsel van Oosten/Squiver.com**.

MAESTRANI Himbeer box background **Holbox/Shutterstock.com**. Close-up of poured chocolate **Liv friis-larsen/Shutterstock.com**. Cows grazing (Switzerland) **Jirsak/Shutterstock.com**. Close-up of strawberries **Ravl/Shutterstock.com**. All other images **Maestrani**.

MENAKO shop display **World Chocolate Awards**. All other images **Menakao**.

MEYBONA Map **Eyespeak/Shutterstock.com**. Cassowary **Dean Bertoncelj/Shutterstock.com**. All other images **Meybona**.

MORIN CHOCOLATERIE A Flush leafs **Evert-Jan/Choqoa.com**. Franck Morin inspecting beans, fermentation box and drying beans; Franck, farmer and tree (Peru); Franck inspecting young tree (Peru) **Chocolaterie A. Morin**. Boat loaded with rice (Mekong) **Don Tran/Shutterstock.com**. Giant tree (Mekong) **Juha Sompinmäki/Shutterstock.com**. Sunset boats (Halong Bay) **Luciano Mortula/Shutterstock.com**. Terraced rice fields (Sapa) **Cyril Hou/Shutterstock.com**.Hut (Mai Chau Village) **Carl Jani/Shutterstock.com**. Chocolate bars **Mikael Damkier/Shutterstock.com**. Bolivia flag **Yui/Shutterstock.com**.

NAIVE All images **Naive**.

ORQUIDEA Chocolate box **World Chocolate Awards**. Coconut **Magicinfoto/Shutterstock.com**.All other images **Orquidea**.

PATRIC All images, excluding chocolate bar packaging **Patric**.

PIERRE MARCOLINI *Chocolat Blanc* All images (including Père Noël bas-relief; Fancy Christmas Tree; Boule de Noël; Grande Sphere Noël; Petit Sapin; Père Noël) **Pierre Marcolini**. *Sans Sucres Ajoutés* Chocolate bar packaging **Pierre Marcolini**. *Plasir Breakfast* Yan Pennor's; Plasir Breakfast bar **World Chocolate Awards**. Plasir Breakfast bar packaging; chef pouring chocolate **Pierre Marcolini**. *Lait* Decorating Easter eggs **Lee McCoy/Chocolatiers.co.uk** Scooping chocolate from the mill **World Chocolate Awards** All other images **Pierre Marcolini**. *Java Lait* Sapin de Noël (dark chocolate balls), Cake Chocolat; shop interior **Pierre Marcolini**.

PRALUS All images of François Pralus; painting cacao sack **Pralus**.

RED STAR Duffy adding sugar to conche **Red Star**.

RAUSCH Chocolate bar packaging background **Scisetti Alfio/Shutterstock.com**. All other images **Rausch**.

ROCOCO Organic Milk bar marble background **mg1408/Shutterstock.com**. Organic Milk bar packaging; Létang Fils chocolate moulds (Ian Whitaker collection) **World Chocolate Awards**. All other images **Rococo**.

ROUX LE HENRI Julien Gouzien portrait **Sonia Lorec**. All other images excluding Yuzu Macha bar and shop sign **Henri Le Roux**.

SALDAC Coffee in hands **Tnewpix/Shutterstock.com**. Ripe coffee branch **Matuchaki/Shutterstock.com**. Amazon ariel view; clouds reflecting on Amazon; bird of prey (Peru) **PearlyV**. Unripe coffee branch **Tropper2000/Shutterstock.com**. Cacao flower **Dr. Morley Read/Shutterstock.com**. Tambopata river bank (Peru) **MP cz/Shutterstock.com**. Butterfly (Peru) **Inyucho**. Hoatzin (Peru) **Carine06**.

SAROTTI Vanilla orchid **VadiCo/Shutterstock.com**. Cured Madagascan Bourbon vanilla pods **Foodpicture/Shutterstock.com**. Vanilla flower **Kschrei/Shutterstock.com**. Chocolate bar packaging **Sarotti**.

SCHARFFEN BERGER John Scharffenberger next to conveyor **Gabriela Hasbun/The Image Bank/Getty Images**. "Scharffen Berger Chocolate Maker" sign writing **Orphanjones**. Close up of mill wheel refining cocoa beans into chocolate (Scharffen Berger) **Eyspahn**. "Scharffen Berger chocolate maker" sign with melangeur motif board (San Francisco) **Chris Saulit**. All other images **Scharffen Berger**.

SLITTI Alberto Rava arranging Ferri Vecchi and all other images **World Chocolate Awards**.

TCHO Trailer and Timothy Childs **Joi Ito**. Portrait of Louis Rossetto at NEXT Berlin **Sebastian Mühlig sebastianmuehlig.de (used under license from NEXT Berlin nextberlin.eu)**. Boxes containing chocolate bars; grabbing chocolate bars **Sebastiaan ter Burg**.

THEO Jane Goodall with Gombe chimpanzee **Michael Neugebauer (used under license from Jane Goodall Institute)**. Glitter watching her sister Gaia fish for termites in Gombe National Park **Jane Goodall Institute**. Jane Goodall "Roots & Shoots" project planting trees (Singapore) **Chris Dickinson (used under license from Jane Goodall Institute)**. All other images **Theo**.

TIROLER EDLE Pouring chocolate **Kaband/Shutterstock.com**. Mountain chalets (Tyrol) **Santi Rodriguez/Shutterstock.com**. Calf face to face with cow **Loribut/Shutterstock.com**. Cable lift milk urns (Tyrol) **Eder/Shutterstock.com**. Gate (Tyrol) **AMB/Shutterstock.com**. Mountain flowers; milk urns stowed upside down **Paul/Shutterstock.com**. All other images, excluding 48% Ohne box **Tiroler Edle**.

VESTRI Grapes **Joanne Harris and Daniel Bubnich/Shutterstock.com**. Vineyard (Tuscany) **Samot/Shutterstock.com**.

VINTAGE PLANTATIONS Whole Milk box background **Tischenko Irina/Shutterstock.com**. Milk with Roasted Peanuts box background **Serg64/Shutterstock.com**. Harvested peanut **Sunsetman/Shutterstock.com**. Peanut farm **Santanor/Shutterstock.com**. Cacao leafs in forest (Ecuador) **Dr Morley Read/Shutterstock.com**. Coffee bush **Fel1ks/Shutterstock.com**. All other images **Vintage Plantations**.

VIVANI Puffed rice **Louella938/Shutterstock.com**. All other images **Vivani**.

WILLIES CACAO Brick background **Vladitto/Shutterstock.com**. All other images **Willie's Cacao**.

ZOTTER All images, excluding chocolate bar packaging **Zotter**.

All images not listed above are the property of the World Chocolate Awards.

www.worldchocolateawards.com

Editor: Ian Whitaker. Editorial Assistant: Erika Whitaker. Evaluator: Ian Whitaker. Proofreaders: Eileen Whitaker, Roger Whitaker. Photography consultant: Joshua Murray. Thanks to Anibal Ayala (Aprocacaho) Honduras, Dr Andrew Daymond (University of Reading), Aroldo Dubon (FHIA) Honduras, CATIE Costa Rica, and Eladio Pop in Belize for their assistance regarding information about cacao.

Published by Infinite Dreams Publishing, Box 32, SK17 9LY, England. Printed and bound in England.

ISBN 978-0-9541355-9-1